Sculpting Type

Edo Smitshuijzen

Sculpting Type

Khatt Books, Amsterdam

Contents

1 Introduction

This publication is, surprisingly, the first book on creating 3d typography using cnc (computer numerical control) machines. Type for 3d applications has always been an orphan in the design profession, catching only the attention of primarily crafts people. Although a few type designers believe that learning how to carve type is essential to become a master designer, most type (and graphic) designers seem to be more comfortable staying in the 2d zone. The daily practice of type design deals with the minutiae of letterforms in two dimensions, first, to make them into a coherent series of original letterforms and second, how to represent these in the best way on screen or in print. In practically all cases, there are no considerations whatsoever for 3d applications. Not even for signage.

The three dimensional aspects of type production have almost totally disappeared since moveable type became obsolete. Today, type production is mostly a complex symphony made visible in ever smaller dots. It is amazing to see how much ingenuity type designers and technicians have put over time in arranging these dots to create the best possible image of type representation on screen. These efforts have become obsolete with the high resolution screens of today. Alongside this, engraving and carving type has been around for the longest time, but these techniques stayed firmly in the domain of craft. Designers were hardly ever interested in this field. It is hard to believe that with the immense amount of different typefaces around, almost none is specifically designed for realisation in 3d. The author of this book has designed a number of 3d typefaces himself for the simple reason that there were no type designs available to show possible applications. There is still a lot of uncharted territory in the professional field of type design. Never mind the fact that hundreds of new type designs are released every day, most are only stylistic exercises.

This book is an attempt to enhance the interest in 3d typography. After all, there are many different ways to use the same digital data used for 2d reproduction for manufacturing in 3d as well. Producing tangible stuff has never been easier. It has become shockingly simple to employ for 3d production almost all types of digital data we use daily. An immense collection of different types of cnc cutters can reproduce practically all types of files in material as thin as paper (and as small as a fly) or up to centimetres thick glass, stone, metal, or whatever other material you fancy in sizes up to building high. Special software has been developed to make even simple cnc routers into machines that can produce truly amazing looking stuff.

'Additive Manufacturing' (or 3d Printing, or Rapid Prototyping, or Stereo Lithography) are the names used for the latest branch of the ever growing technology tree. It will make manufacturing a desktop activity. This technology has effectively eliminated all traditional production constraints. Every possible shape can be produced as long as it doesn't collapse under its own weight.

This now easily accessible territory of producing tangible stuff is anxiously waiting for designers with graphic and communication skills to dream away and explore this new universe that is much less ephemeral than their traditional professional field. Their creative background may move traditional barriers. Our environment may be enriched with tangible objects from a world of creation normally exposed in books, magazines or on screens. This book is an invitation for designers to make this happen. It explains the basic different technologies of manufacturing to be used, discusses production options, problems and how to deal with them best. But most of all, by showcasing new designs the author tries to open up the lid of a bottomless box that has stayed closed for too long.

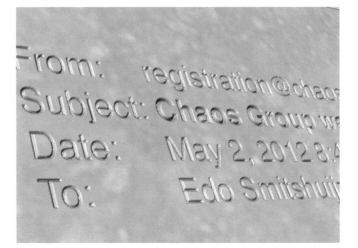

Digitisation of all production and communication has created a world where every sign of life once captured in a digital format can be converted easily into production instructions for practically all kinds of fabrication: your shopping list or email message can be cut in marble and the snapshot on your digital camera or phone can be woven in damask. Picture left top: lace portrait by Pierre Fouché, right top self portrait by Joe Lewis, underneath an email message cut in sandstone.

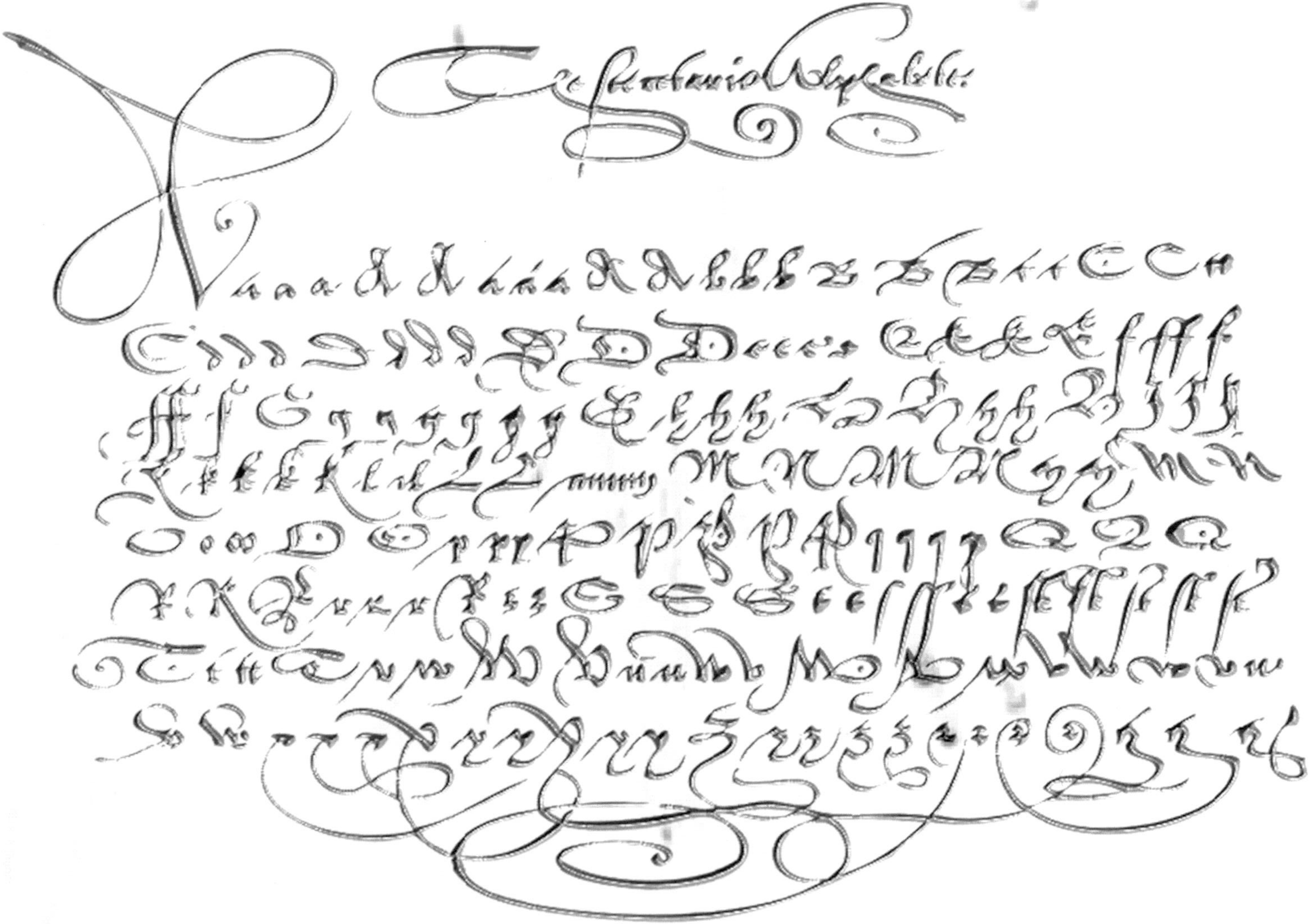

2 The shape of letters

Ink, pen and paper were for long the basic ingredients to write letters. Letters that could be combined into words, which in turn could be arranged to form sentences. Finally, sentences can be grouped to make small notes or large encyclopaedias, and anything in between. The written word is at the base of human civilisation. Most of it is no longer handwritten and the speed of text production today is on a par with the speed of light. Yet, type still bears the traces of its handwritten past. For some typestyles these traces are obvious, other styles have emerged through centuries of industrial type manufacturing which developed its own set of requirements depending on the technologies applied. Type for the Latin script in particular has been influenced by numerous designers who anticipated in their type designs the latest changes in production technology and ever changing style fads. Type for the Arabic script, by contrast, stayed in general closer to its calligraphic source. With the emancipation of Arabic type design, Arabic type is likely to stray away further from the original handwritten shapes and to evolve from the commercial and technical constraints of today's text production.

The image on the left page illustrates today's options for design and production. The internet is a limitless source of easy downloadable images. Drawing software can automatically trace silhouettes of images and generate spline outlines that can be scaled to any size without losing quality. Production software almost instantly creates from these outlines tool paths for v-carving, for instance, and generates an image of how it will look like in reality and how long it will take to manufacture at a given size. Desktop cnc machines can actually do the manufacturing. All this can be produced within one hour.

Writing tools

The tools originally used for text production clearly had a large influence on the shape of letters. The broad nib steel pen and the goose quill were for centuries the instruments of choice to produce texts and handmade books. Their influence on the shape of the Latin script therefore has been large. The pointy steel pen and the burin are the two other important writing tools which were hugely influential. The pencil, the paintbrush and the chisel surely had an impact on the type designs. The chisel is often held responsible for the appearance of the 'serifs' in the Latin script. But the brush and the pencil played in the Latin script only a supporting role to produce the more elaborated forms of writing. Many Asian cultures favoured the paintbrush over any type of pen. The Chinese script is a sample of this tradition.

For the Arabic script, writing tools were often used in combination. The reed pen is the basic writing instrument and is cut at a different angle than used for the Latin script. However, not all letters can easily be drawn with this tool alone. A number of individual letters need some extra attention from a paintbrush or a pointy pen to get their final desired shape. This gives the Arabic script a less disciplined and more flowery visual style than the Latin script.

The broad nibbed pen, the pointy nibbed pen and the paintbrush are the basic style makers for all scripts. Some styles are produced by a combination of the three basic tools. The burin and the chisel have a characteristic of their own, but create in effect derivative forms in three dimensions of the shapes produced with the three basic writing instruments.

The elements of a font
The basic parts of any alphabetic writing system are the collection of individual signs that comprise the alphabet. Both Arabic and Latin are alphabetic writing systems. The alphabet alone is not sufficient for a writing system to function, we need punctuation marks to create easy to read sentences and we use accents or diacritics to add extra letters (variations) to the alphabet. Next, we have added an ever growing number of signs and symbols for scientific, mathematical or other purposes, the collection of ten numbers being the most basic addition. The amount of individual signs (glyphs) that are part of a font have been standardised. This standard is not 'set in stone' and changes over time, but two big American companies: Microsoft and Adobe, effectively set the standards of the glyphs appearing in most fonts on the basis of the work of the so called 'Unicode Consortium', an international standardisation body.
There are some characteristics that make the languages using the Latin script different to the languages using the Arabic script. In Latin, the alphabet has two important form variations: a set of capital letters and a set of so-called 'lower case' letters. The Arabic script does not have this distinction.

Furthermore, the Latin script has a 'Roman' (straight) and an 'Italic' (cursive) version. The true 'italic' version of the Latin alphabet is based on a different historic calligraphic style so some letter shapes are basically different in both sets. There is also a slanted Roman version (called 'oblique') that is used as an 'Italic' but this variation is less distinctive and therefore less functional. Traditionally, the Arabic script does not have 'Italics' although some Arabic fonts are available in a slanted version.

Ligatures are a combination of two or more letters drawn as one sign (glyph) to make a specific letter combination look nicer. Making ligatures has typically derived from calligraphy where individual letters constantly change shape slightly depending

The broad nibbed pen, the pointy pen and the paint brush were traditionally the basic tools of writing. These tools have influenced the shape of type. Chinese writing is uniquely made with a brush, the Arabic script used a combination of tools and the Latin script is made with a broad nibbed or a pointy pen.

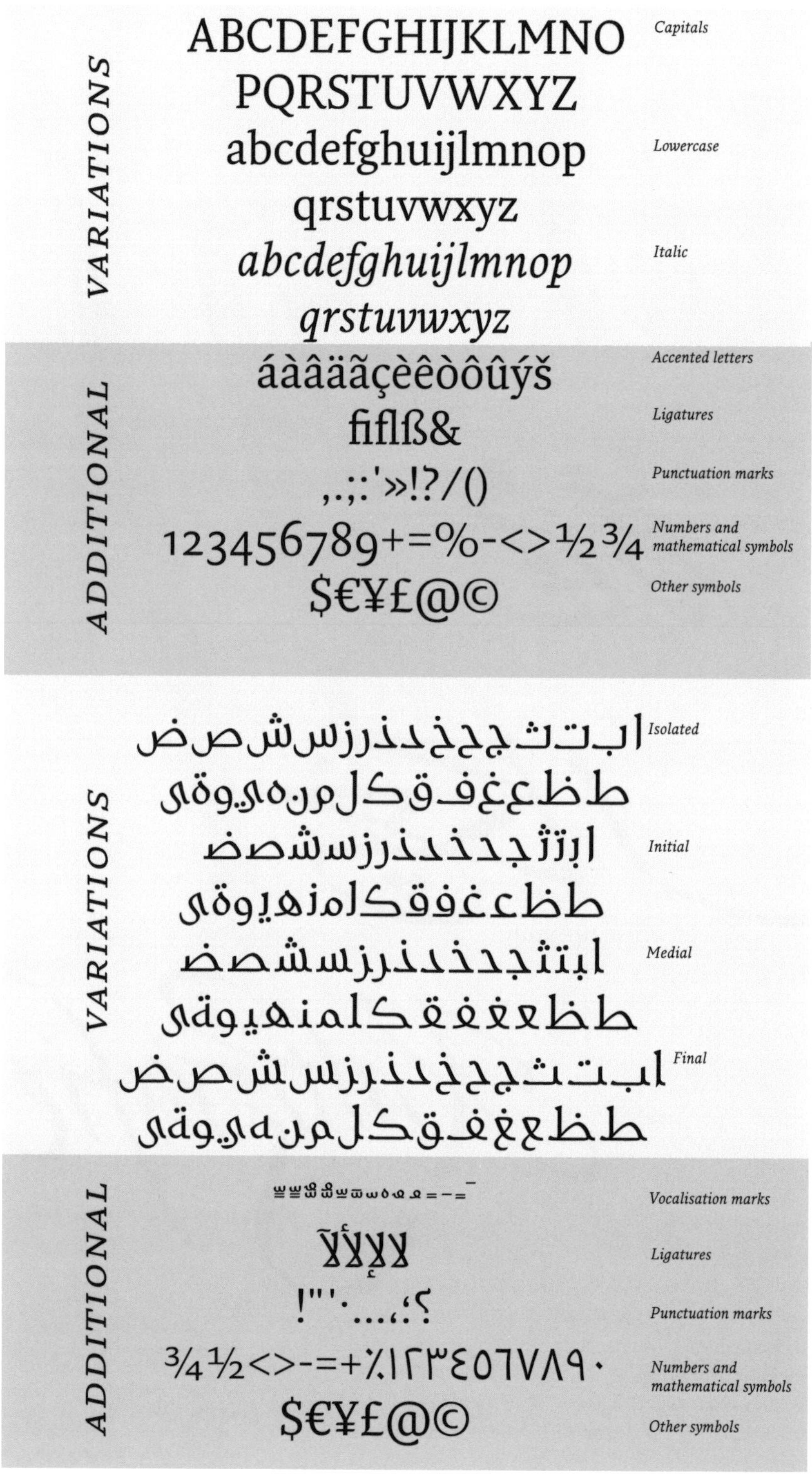

ABCDEFGHIJKLMNO
PQRSTUVWXYZ

Capitals

abcdefghuijlmnop
qrstuvwxyz

Lowercase

*abcdefghuijlmnop
qrstuvwxyz*

Italic

áàâäãçèèêòôûýš

Accented letters

fiflß&

Ligatures

,.;:'»!?/()

Punctuation marks

123456789+=%-<>½¾

Numbers and mathematical symbols

$€¥£@©

Other symbols

ابـتـثـجـجـخـدـذرزسـشـصـض
طظعغـفـقـكـلـمنـهـوةى

Isolated

ابتٱجدذدذرزسـشـصض
طظعغفـفـعـكامزهـيـوةى

Initial

ابتتجدذدذرزسـشـصض
طظعغغعـفـقـكامنـهـيـوةى

Medial

ابـتـثـجـجـخـدـذرزسـشـصـض
طظعغـفـقـكـلـمنـوـدةى

Final

ﹽﹶﹷﹸﹹﹺﹻﹼﹽ ـ = ـ ـ ¯

Vocalisation marks

ﻷﻹﻻﻵ

Ligatures

!"'`،...؛؟

Punctuation marks

¾½<>-=+٪١٢٣٤٥٦٧٨٩٠

Numbers and mathematical symbols

$€¥£@©

Other symbols

on the shape of the neighbouring letters. Calligraphers make the letters in a sentence that appear next to each other dance together in harmony. Each letter accommodates its neighbours. Fonts for the Arabic script kept more of its traditional ligatures than the Latin script. The ligatures in Arabic have become in some instances signs on their own. In these cases, the original combination of letters is hardly recognisable. In Latin we have only very few of those type of ligatures. The '&' sign started as a ligature of the Latin word 'et', meaning 'and'. Over time, Western manufacturers of typesetting machines for the Arabic script have constructed complicated machines to accommodate the need for a large array of ligatures in the Arabic script. Today's digital technology makes the use of ligatures much easier, resulting in more ligatures appearing in Latin fonts and a revival of calligraphic fonts. The technical problems that always accompanied Arabic typesetting are now a thing of the past.

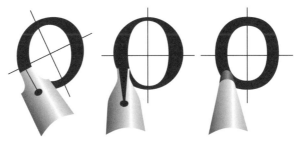

Type style classification

Since the beginning of the previous century, various attempts have been made to classify type styles for the Latin script: Francis Thibaudeau (1921), Maximilien Vox (1952), the International organisation of type designers Atypi (1962), German Standardisation Bureau, DIN (1964), Aldo Novarese (1964). The most important general distinction in Latin type styles is the distinction between text types and display types. The first category includes all type that can be used to create easy readable text for newspapers, books and magazines. The second is type for headlines and short messages to draw the attention or create a specific atmosphere. The second important distinction is between the serifs and sans-serifs. Serifs are small extensions on the end stroke of certain letter parts. 'Serifs' have these extensions, 'sans serifs' don't. Today, the 'mix' is a type style between the serifs and sans-serifs. The third important style distinction is the level of 'letter contrast': the difference between the thickness of the thinnest part of the letter and the thickest part. Type with a very low contrast are called linears or stroke fonts. For the rest, historic styles are used to indicate a style distinction. The most used is 'Antiqua' or 'Old Style' to indicate classical styles. The shape of the serif is used as indication and a separate category are the type styles that are still very close to handwriting. Today's type foundries use all kinds of classifications to categorise their at times gigantic collection of fonts. There are so many 'in between' hybrid styles that any classification system for typefaces has only a limited value.

The three basic styles for Latin type and their matching writing tools. Left, the broad nibbed pen and the 'Antiqua', or 'Old Face' style. Middle, the pointy steel pen and the 'Modern Face'. Right, the ball point or pencil and the 'Grotesk' or 'Linear' style.

The illustration on the left page gives an overview of the differences between the basic 'glyph' collection in an Arabic versus a Latin font. Please observe that some modern Arabic fonts have reduced the amount of traditional ligatures dramatically.

Style classification for Arabic type is still based on the original calligraphic styles, like Naskh, Kufi, Thuluth, Maghribi, Ruqaa, Diwani and Nastaliq. The Naskh style is by far the most popular for Arabic type. In fact, most type for the Arabic script is designed in the Naskh style. The more geometric Kufi style is a good second in style preference and is mostly used for architectural applications and for headlines and logos. The new generation

The fundamental difference in type style for the Latin script is between the 'serifs' and 'sans-serifs'. Serifs are small extensions at the end of letter strokes. The shape of the serifs are an important indication for further style classification.

of Arab type designers are often inspired by both styles to make their type designs. The amount of well designed Latin type available today is overwhelming. Of course, there is also the landfill size of trash quality around. The development of a new typeface used to be a large investment in the old days. That is no longer the case, resulting in a landslide of new (or revival) typefaces. There are a lot of gems to find between the casual rubble that comes with any landslide.

Ligatures are a combination of two or more letters written as one single sign (glyph). The ampersand (left) is a ligature—the combination of the letters 'e' and 't', meaning 'and'—with the status of a symbol, next is the double 's' ligature, much used in German, next is a 'ct' ligature. Following, are three samples for the Arabic script, which has a rich tradition for using complicated ligatures, often combining three or more letters, put not only next—but also on top—of each other.

Arabic type design is still in its infancy. It's a gold mine for young type designers. Some traditional calligraphic styles are practically unexplored territory for type designers and there is plenty of room for well designed Arabic type. Large countries, like Iran and Pakistan use the Arabic script for their own languages and have their own indigenous calligraphic traditions. Also in these countries type design is just anxiously waiting to come to full blossom.

هي كطوع المشعلادن

Kufi

هي كطوع المشعلادر

Eastern Kufi

هي كطوع المشعلادن

Naskh

هي كطوع المشعلادن

Thuluth

هى كطوع المشعلادن

Nastalic

اهى كطوع المشعلادكاز

Diwani

هي كطوع المشتعلادهن

Maghrebi

هى كطوع المشعلادن

Ruqaa

A concise overview of the major calligraphic/
type styles used with the Arabic script. The
Naskh style is by far the most used. The Kufi
style is a good second in popularity. Young
type designers are inspired to create new
hybrid styles by mixing the Naskh and Kufi
style.

The Naskh Style

Naskh is by far the most popular text face. It usually attempts to come close to the calligraphic style, including many ligatures. The 'Simplified Naskh' is far more austere, even limited to only two variations per character.

Yakout *was the first Simplified Naskh typeface. It follows the Naskh structure but uses only two variations per character. It is usually used in newspaper design.*

Lotus *is a typical Naskh typeface and is usually used in books.*

Palatino Arabic *is also a Naskh typeface but it has larger counters and an extensive ligature set.*

Badiya *is a Neo Naskh because it follows the Naskh structure but treats the outlines in a modern way.*

The Kufi Style

Kufi is the oldest calligraphic style of the Arabic script. Many Kufi styles are geometric and/or decorative and therefore mostly used for headlines. They usually have only one (Lam-Alef) ligature.

Ahmed *is a typical Kufi typeface as can be seen by its structure. Its Mim shape shows another possible structural variation for this character.*

Kufi *says it all by its own name. This typeface is highly ornamental and is suitable for use in large sizes.*

Isra *is a Neo Kufi which means that its basic structure is a Kufi, but the treatment of the outlines is modern.*

Frutiger Arabic *is a humanist Kufi. It follows the Kufi structure but also incorporates structural and outline treatment of cursive styles such as Naskh and Ruqaa.*

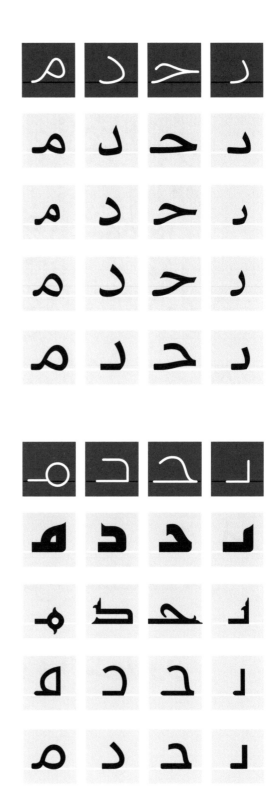

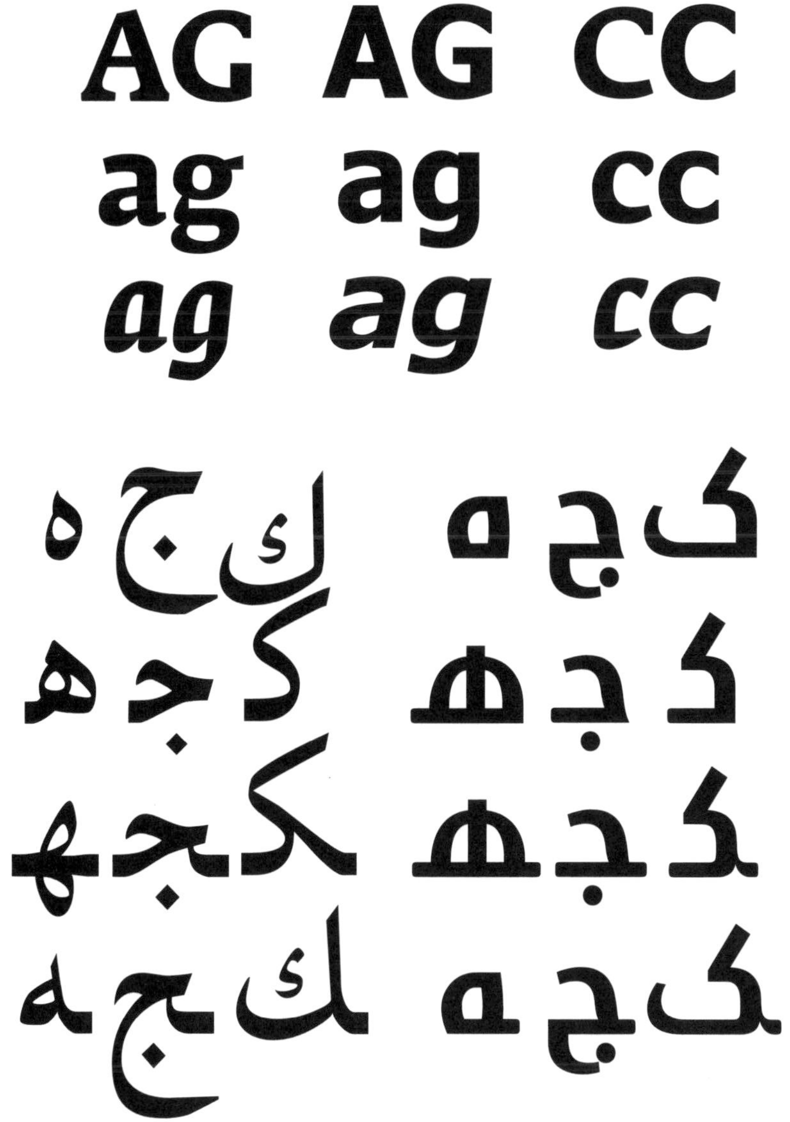

AG AG CC
ag ag cc
ag *ag* *cc*

كـ جـ ه
ك جـ هـ
ك جـ ه
ك جـ ه

On the left page: a brief overview by Nadine Chahine of the major style differences between the two most used type styles: Naskh and Kufi.

One single alphabetical letter may appear in quite different shapes. On top, the Latin script has three basic shape variations for each letter: a capital, lower case and an italic version. The difference between these variations can be large or small depending on the type style and the specific letter selected to make the comparison.

The left column on top shows the largest possible variation in shape, the letters 'a' and 'g' in a 'serif' typeface. The non-serif version in the next column shows already less variation. The letter 'c' in the following column shows

hardly any variation in shape.

The differences in shape of identical letters in the Arabic alphabet is much bigger than in the Latin alphabet. First, there are four basic shape variations of each letter: the isolated, initial, medial and the final version of a letter's position in a word. Second, the type style selected may change the letter shape dramatically. In the left column the three letters 'ha', 'jeem' and 'kaf' in the Naskh style. In the next column, the same letters shown in the Kufi style.

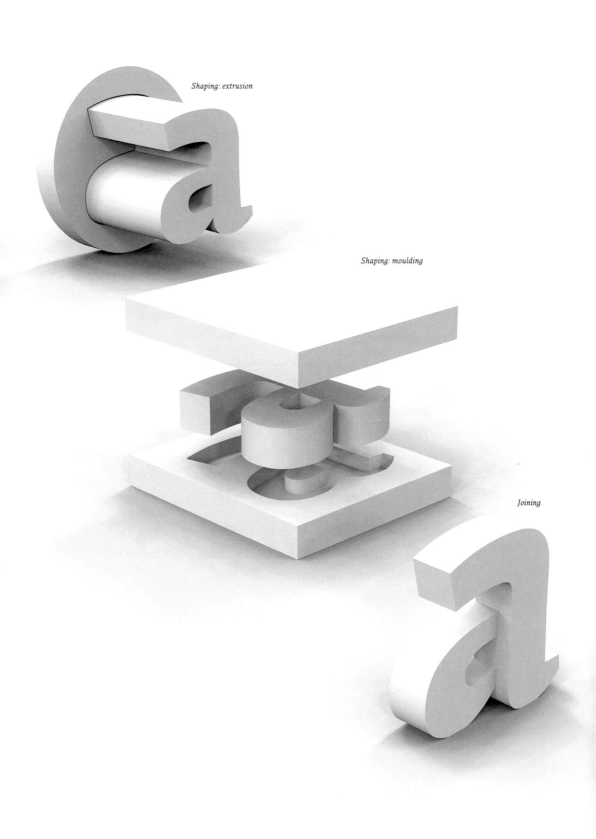

Shaping: extrusion

Shaping: moulding

Joining

3 Shaping technologies

At some level of sophistication or other, practically all industrial production today is 'computer numerically controlled' (cnc) and therefore all production machines now in use are more or less cnc machines. Nevertheless, there is a large discrepancy between production that is 'die or mould based' versus production that is based on manufacturing a series of 'one-offs' (each product is individually machined). The last method is obviously the way of producing for the future, since it is extremely flexible, allows for customising and avoids the preproduction of costly dies. In many ways, the technologies of the future will bring back the manufacturing options of pre-industrial handmade production, only this time fabrication is done at an immensely higher speed.

Left page, two major shaping technologies: extrusion and moulding, plus the important technology of joining fabricated parts together.

The fusion of design and manufacturing
The preliminary phase of actual industrial production, the design phase, has become ever closer linked to manufacturing. Digitisation of both phases brought the two together. CAD/CAM (Computer Aided Design and Manufacturing) is in fact how all fabrication is currently carried out. Designers and inventors still use pencils to scribble their ideas on paper, but soon thereafter their design proposals will be 'put into a computer' not only to test their ideas, but also to make them visually better presentable and to be able to disseminate the design proposals quite easily. Today's teamwork is based on the availability of digital files. Design and actual production have become almost seamlessly intertwined. The advantages are obvious; the disadvantages somewhat less. When a design can be presented on a computer screen it is by definition immediately translatable in very precise numeric data, because computers only accept numeric data. So, in principle, all information is available to actually produce the design. Of course a fantastic opportunity for designers, but it can easily lead to a computer addiction, possibly ending in a nasty delirium. The image on the computer screen tends to dictate what will be manufactured in the end. This process has already taken place for

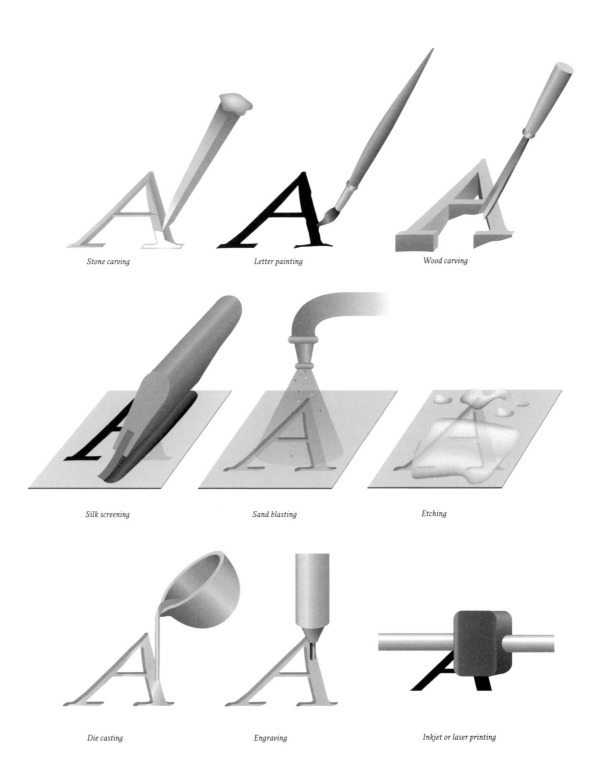

Stone carving

Letter painting

Wood carving

Silk screening

Sand blasting

Etching

Die casting

Engraving

Inkjet or laser printing

A concise overview of techniques for creating letterforms: traditional manual techniques, masking methods, moulding, engraving and printing.

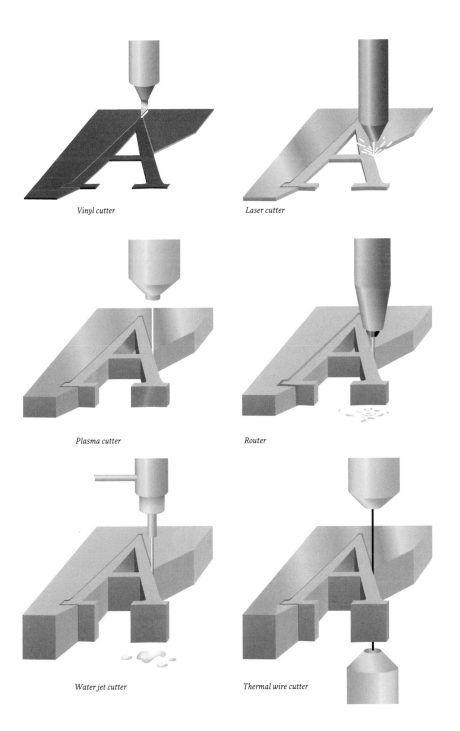

Vinyl cutter

Laser cutter

Plasma cutter

Router

Water jet cutter

Thermal wire cutter

A concise overview of the large variety of cutting machines currently available. Water jet cutters have gained popularity because of their wide range of applications.

some time. Just look around; it would have been better for much of manufactured stuff to have remained as an image on screen where it simply looks more attractive than in the material world.

General categories of production

There are in principle three basic technologies available for product manufacturing: shaping, joining and finishing technologies. Each of these categories employ an already large, but still ever growing variety of different techniques. Shaping comprises all technologies to alter the shape of basic materials. Joining combines basic materials or parts of products. And finishing concerns itself with the look and feel of the outer skin of a product.

Extrusion and moulding

The Industrial Revolution created production methods where a large part of the initial production costs were in the creation of the dies (moulds) and the adaptation of machines that could handle these dies. The two major techniques were extrusion and moulding (also called die-casting). Extrusion is the creation of profiled bars by pressing base material through an opening that has a specific shape. It creates effectively 2D shapes at long lengths that can be cut afterwards to any desired length. It is a much used and relative cheap production method because the dies are relatively cheap and extruding material is fast.

Moulds are more expensive to manufacture, although cnc mould production has made them cheaper. The variety of production methods based on moulds seems almost endless, but basically material is poured or pressed in a mould and released afterwards, leaving a complete product or a part of it.

Moulding techniques were—and still are—also used to create one-offs. Bonze sculptures (or church bells) for instance are made with a mould that can only be used once (cire-perdue). Also for production of lettering and name plaques, moulding techniques were once popular. Modular systems that allow for easy assembly of a large variety of sign panels are often made from extruded slats.

Cutters

Cutters cut any 2D shape out of practically all types of flat material. Almost all industrial cutting today is done using cnc machines. The cutting techniques available are many: laser, plasma, waterjet, the good old (mini) knife and routers, among others. Waterjet cutting gained popularity because there are hardly any restrictions on the materials to be used, heat generation (potentially resulting in deformation of the flat material) is no problem and the cutting line can remain relatively thin and smooth. Most cutters cut completely through the material. Lasers and—of course—routers can also be used as engraving machines where only a part of the top layer of the material is effected.

Cutters and routers are the technology of choice for sign manufacturing. Specifically, vinyl cutters will be found in the workshop

Opposite page, the three basic shaping technologies: die casting, tooling or machining and the so-called 'additive production', or 3d printing. Die casting may speed up production, but dies are expensive and do not allow for customising. Machining became much more attractive after the computer could take over the navigation of the bits and tools. Customising became easy, but chipping away material from a panel or a solid block remains somewhat cumbersome.
Additive production seems to have the best of both worlds: ideal for customising and no rest material or chips.

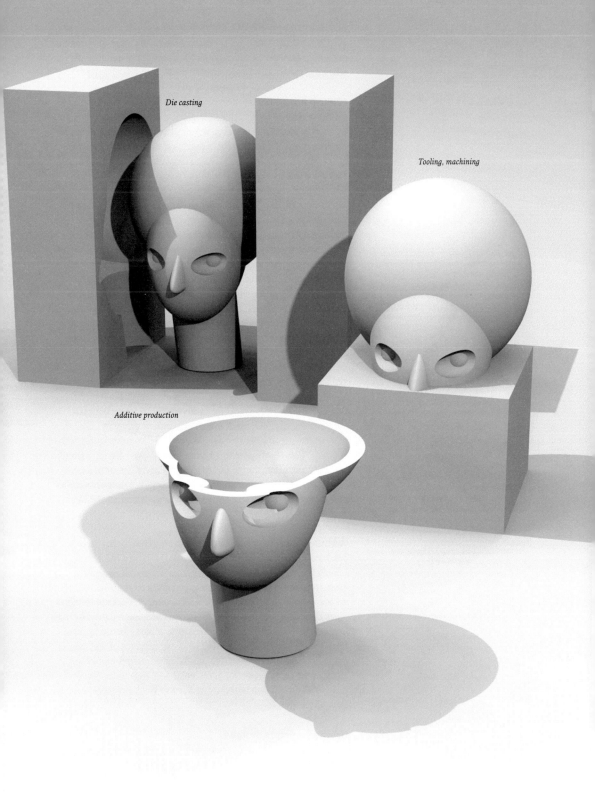

Die casting

Tooling, machining

Additive production

of almost all sign manufacturers. Adhesive vinyls are now available in so many varieties that any conceivable application can be served. In fact, all constraints related to indoor or outdoor use, or size have practically disappeared.

Milling machines

Milling machines use various methods to model solid materials by cutting away little pieces at a time. The lathe rotates the material and keeps the cutting tools fixed and the router works the other way around. Milling machines come in endless varieties. Most of them use hardened tool bits to cut away the material. Cnc milling has gained popularity over complex injection moulding, because a mould in not easy to change, while the software instructions to steer the milling tools can easily be reprogrammed. Small changes in the design can be implemented fast and relatively easily. Customised production is relatively easy. That is why the housing of the Apple notebooks, for instance is now milled out of solid aluminum.

Rapid prototyping

Machines in this category come with all kind of names, 3d printing, selective laser sintering, stereo lithography, electron beam melting and solid freeforming for instance. A solid model is built up layer by layer by melting, dissolving or hardening material. This fabrication was originally developed for producing a completely functional prototype in a fast and cheap way. Today, these types of machines are used for industrial production of small series and completely customised one-offs. A growing number of products are offered that are produced with 'prototyping' techniques. The advantage of this technology is large, because there is hardly any limitation to the complexity and the sort of shapes that can be produced, production technology is relatively simple, and all basic material will be put into the end product—no lost material and no chips.

'Additive Manufacturing' is another name given to this type of production. Supposedly, it may start off the 'Third Industrial Revolution' of 'Mass-Customising'. Machines of this type are already on the market in a desktop size. When combined with a 3d scanner, these machines can work wonders, because broken parts of existing tools or equipment can easily be repaired by replicating the broken piece. Keeping stock of parts would become obsolete. This technology would be the equivalent of the 'print-on-demand' which made large-run book printing—and keeping stock of the edition—no longer needed.
Industrial production without the need to keep any stock would be a revolution, indeed.

Other shaping techniques

A vast array of other shaping techniques exist that use electric current, chemical substances or pressure to shape solid or sheet

Opposite page, additive production methods are available in a wide range. All share a few basic principles. A product is built up in very thin (0.1 mm) horizontal layers. A production nozzle/print head moves over the x and y axes to create the footprint of any individual layer. A horizontal plate lifts or lowers the object over the z axis in increments of the thickness of each layer.
The advantage of additive production over the subtracting (chipping away) alternative is that the first needs no more than these three axes to produce everything imaginable. The latter needs five and is still hampered by the fact that tool bits need access. The advantage of the subtracting technology is the freedom of choice of material.

The illustration shows three major technologies. The difference between them is the basic material employed and the technology in the printer head. With laser sintering the laser in the head melts a thin layer of the basic granular material. Stereo lithography uses uv light to harden the top layer of a container filled with liquid photopolymer. With polyjet the production nozzle prints the heated basic material itself. This material can be any kind of plastic. A photopolymer can be printed and hardened directly thereafter by uv light, but the nozzle can also be fed with a thin tube of plastic, heated up and extruded. A bit like a glue gun.

These technologies can be used to make end products but also moulds. By mixing all kind of production methods, products can be made in a very large range of materials.

Laser sintering

Stereo lithography

Polyjet printing

materials, sometimes with the help of a mould.

Shaping software

To make cnc machines run the way you want them to, you need two types of software. First, you need to produce your design by creating minimally a two dimensional digital outline of the shape you wish to cut, rout or extrude. Second, you need to transform this shape into a 'toolpath' for the tool bits to be used to make the shape of your design in the material at hand. The programming language for cnc machines for steering the tool bits is called 'G code'.

The two dimensional outlines for your designs can be produced by many drawing software around. Almost anybody can use this type of software today. But this level of creation is only in two dimensions, not three. Designing with 3d modelling software is a bit more complex. This type of software is more sophisticated and has a steeper learning curve. A steep learning curve is in most cases also an indication that there is room for further sophistication of the software's interface. If you compare 2d modelling with bending one metal wire to a desired shape on a flat surface; 3d modelling requires a more or less dense mesh of wires like a tea strainer to contain all information. Architects, product designers and animation specialists all use professional 3d modelling software, which has reached a level of amazing technical sophistication. The distinction between the real world and the fabricated one has effectively disappeared. This impressive capacity is not only due to making extremely complex mesh wires, but also because the related 'rendering' software can dress these wire constructions with near real life surfaces and the lighting software can imitate reality amazingly well. However, this highly sophisticated level of creation can only be reached by well trained professionals.

For beginners, there are free, shareware or open source packages around. At student level inexpensive modelers are for sale and there are many different packages at the high end professional level. CAD/CAM (computer aided design/computer aided manufacturing) software packages exist in a lot of varieties to create specific type of products. There is a close link between modelling software and 3d computer animation. Although each has its own distinctive purpose, animation software is 'surface' oriented and modelling software is 'solid' oriented.

The most up-market 3d software is not only used to create precise 3d models, the software extends further and further in all aspects related to manufacturing, like the constructive strength of a design, the die costs and flow of material in different methods of production. Specialised modelling software is now even extending to the commercial and maintenance aspects of a design.

Cnc modelling for small workshops and hobby

Just as it happened before with professional publishing software,

CAD/CAM software became available in a 'desktop' variety; a version of computer aided design and manufacturing that was specifically directed at small workshop owners and hobbyists. The level of this software and the related cnc machines are constantly improving. This type of software lets you create your own 2d outlines, but it has also modelling options. After a design is made, it can be rendered and made visible, so you will have a realistic

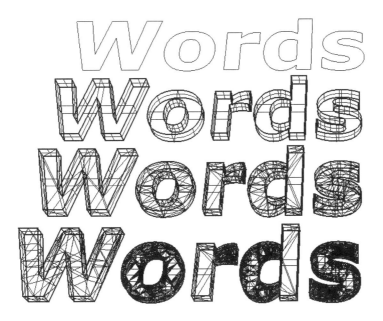

visual impression of how your design will look after production. Hereafter, the file can be converted in (machine) g code specifically for a listed set of cnc machines available on the market.

What has happened with 'publishing' software is very likely to happen again with 'product manufacturing'. Designers will be capable of doing their own production. Rapid prototyping machines and small robots will become more and more sophisticated and lower in price. The distinction between the professional product designer and the amateur will blur over time.

Not only desktop sized 3d printers will be available, but also very large sized ones. Maybe building construction will some day also start to use computerised 'additive production' technology. Imagine a building site where the basic construction of floors/ceilings and walls will be 'printed' by a cnc navigated nozzle pouring out concrete or mortar as material.

Cutting machines and cnc routers only need the simplest of files to work from, an outline is all it needs (illustration on top). When a cutter is used, the third dimension is determined by the thickness of the material selected. For cnc routers, the third dimensional shape is also determined by the shape of the tool bit selected and the specified cutting depth.

Modelling software is required to create files all other production methods can work with. Each software has its own format for describing 3 dimensional objects (second illustration from top). This format can be converted into a meshed structure so it can be rendered in a halftone picture or used by other machines and software. There is the option to select the number of meshes to be used (the two illustration at the bottom). The more meshes, the more refined the surface will be. It is comparable to the pixel resolution of a picture. There are a number of different file formats for 3d file exchange.

4 Designing for cnc production

The way we do—and make—things has gone through dramatic changes during our recent history. Disseminating written messages used to take lot of effort during almost the entire development of human civilisation. Today, with internet, Facebook, Twitter and all the other niceties around, that is hard to imagine. Everything related to the basic technology of printing took quite some investment and skilled labour. Now, everyone in the affluent societies has their own production facilities on their table tops. And those manufacturing facilities have perplexingly more production options than any printing facility in history. It is 'normal' that we have hundreds of different typefaces on our computer, for instance. Digital image manipulation has entered a complete new universe compared with the traditional imaging techniques. We got so used to living with abundance that we no longer realise how immensely wealthy we are. One of the core strategies when starting a design project was to first make an inventory of all relevant products or systems around. Regrettably, this sensible way to start has become effectively impossible. There is simply too much stuff around. We have to limit any research phase to what is still feasible to investigate.

Selecting a base technology

Having too many choices is also true for designing for cnc production and will only be more so in the future. The amount of modelling software, and production technologies, and machines around is already immense and it will not get any better. However, there are a number of basic principles of production to choose from before starting the design. First, there are the endless possibilities that 3d printing offers. Anything is possible in the shapes you wish to create, but the amount of base material to select from is still rather limited compared to other production methods and production of bigger sizes become really costly. Second, the next basic choice to make is between using 'cutters' or 'millers'. Cutters shape all kinds of panel material in two

The three dimensional space is defined by the x, y and z axes. Production machines are classified by the maximum size of the workpiece and the number of axes they can handle. For additive production, like 3d printing, movement of the production head in the three basic axes is sufficient to create all possible shapes. For subtractive production, like milling machines, movement in five axes is needed to be able to chip away material at any given angle. The illustration on the opposite page shows those five axes. The x for covering the width of an object, the y for the length, the z for the depth. The two extra a and c axes effectively create the option to tilt a tool bit moving on the x or the y axis to any degree.
(Note that modelling software engineers and their peers in hardware engineering each have their own conventions about which axis to call x, y or z.)

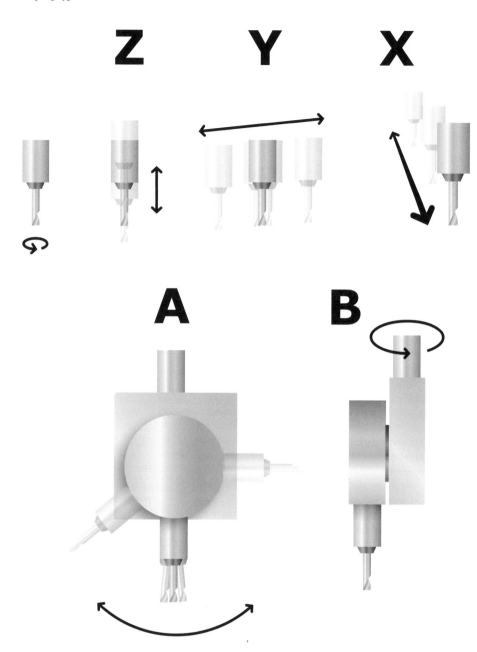

The illustration above shows the movements of the toolbits over the five axes. In this case, the workpiece is fixed in place. The illustration at the top of the opposite right page shows an alternative method, in that case the workpiece (the bed of the machine) is moving over the five axes and the tool bit is fixed in place. Milling machines use all kind of combinations of these two principles, often in combination with revolving toolheads that pick-up different tool bits automatically.

The small illustration on the left bottom of the opposite page shows a typical heavy 5 axes milling machine with a fixed bed. The illustration next to it shows the diagram of the six axes of movement freedom. The basic x, y and z axes have each the option of 360° rotation. The different movements can be described as: z up and down (heaving), y left and right (swaying), x back and forth (surging), b turning left and right (yawing), a tilting forward and backward (pitching), c tilting side to side (rolling).

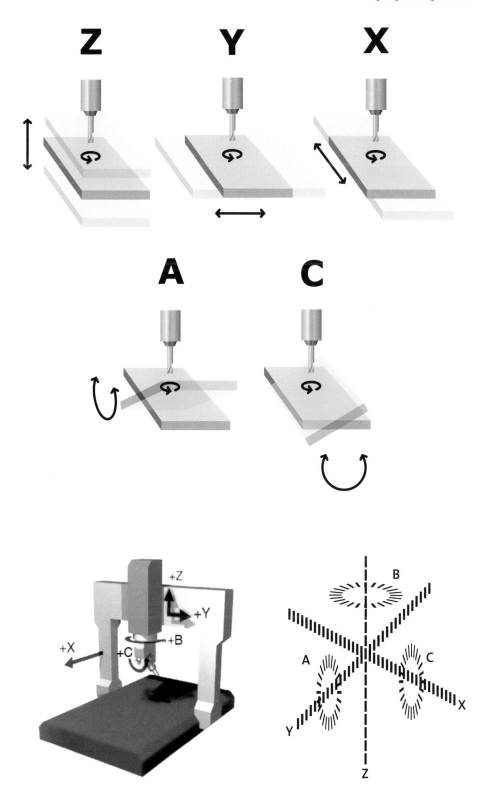

dimensions only while millers can 'chip away' base material in the third dimension also. Obviously, shaping in three dimensions allows for more intricate designs and certainly for more refinement in the detailing.

Cutting machines are by far the most economic to use and will allow for working with big sizes in practically all basic panel or sheet material. Most machines will cut panels in standard industry sizes. The number of different materials to choose from is large. In fact, there is so much variety in synthetic and composite panel material around that it is tough to select the most appropriate one for a job. A special category in between the cutters and the milling machines are the cnc routers. Cutters only work in two dimensions, they just cut all the way through material in a straight line. Cnc routers allow for selecting a specifically shaped tool bit and selection of a cutting depth. Sometimes these machines are called 2.5d machines. Routers are traditional tools. All engraving machines are routers, for instance. Originally, all navigation on these machines was done mechanically, the cutting depth could be fixed and the tool bit navigation was directed by hand from a physical template. With the help of the so-called pantograph arm, all sizes could be produced from the template. Computerisation of the cnc machines took the technology many steps further. Cnc routers take an important place in cnc typography and will therefore be given a separate chapter.

3d milling machines come in an extremely large variety. The major differences between them are the number of 'axes' that can be used for navigation and the sizes they can handle. For the number of axes, the basic choice is between a three axes machine, covering the so-called 'x, y and z-axes'. If you project these axes on a simple rectangular box, the x would be the length, the y the width and the z the height of the box. (In modelling software the convention is somewhat different). In principle, all three dimensional shapes can be constructed using these three axes, but the tool bits of millers can only work perpendicular to any given x, y, or z plane. So, machines with only three axes can only make 'box-like' movements. This limits the shapes that can actually be produced. By adding the option to tilt on both the x and y axe, effectively all shapes can be produced. Obviously, with the limitation that these shapes must be accessible with a tool, so 'enclosed' spaces cannot be produced. 3d printing does not have this restriction.

There are two ways to provide the movement along the various axes: either the tool bit moves in different directions or the workpiece does. Often, a combination of the two is used.

Most milling machines are used to manufacture relatively small objects out of solid metal. Basically, milling machines are used to produce (other) machines or tools. The ones that can handle bigger objects need heavy frames to keep their precision. The forces needed to chip away material from big solid objects are very large, so these machines are big, heavy and expensive. The latest development in milling machines are so-called robots. Actually, merely a robotic arm fixed on a steady platform functioning in combination with a rotation disk on which the workpiece is fixed. This kind of machine is now entering the low end of the market and will most likely 'disrupt' the production of the more costly and heavier machinery.

Cutting machines and cnc routers are by far the most used production methods for 3d typography.

Specifying for the selected technology

Most product designs will be produced in parts that will be assembled together. A variety of technologies are likely to be used to produce these parts. Nevertheless, when working with letters, selecting a production method for the part where the letters will appear is important, because this selection implies how the 'artwork' or the production specification should be delivered. For cnc cutting machines, the specification requirements are basic: the specification of the material to be used and its thickness, a digitised outline of the shapes to be cut out and the size of these shapes. For cutting machines almost any type of artwork will do because halftone artwork can be scanned into a bitmap file which can be traced automatically into outlines.

Cnc routers can also be used as cutting machines, but they can do more. Routers can work with two different type of files: outlines and a large variety of 3d file formats. The way the router deals with these two types of input is fundamentally different. The outlines will be used to navigate the tool bits. But the final shape of the outlines also depends on the shape of the toolbit that is selected and the depth of the cut. These two variables have to be specified separately. Working with outlines on a cnc router is a very efficient way to produce 3d typography. The cnc router can also work with 3d files. In that case, the selection of the tool bits is predetermined and does not have a specific shaping function other than shaping the contours of the workpiece in the z-axis direction. The shape on the 3d file will be chipped away from the solid material in small incremental steps. Often the process will be done in stages: a bigger tool bit will chip away the rough contour of the design. Thereafter, smaller tool bits will refine these contours. The tool bit will move in a straight line over the full length of one side of the plane while following the various ups and downs of the contour of the model over that line. The same operation will be repeated a few millimetres next to the previous one until the other side of the plane is completely covered. This 'slicing method' makes 3d modeling possible with a 3-axes machine.

A 5-axes milling machine can produce much more sophisticated results, but production costs are much higher. In principle, 5-axes machines can put the toolbit perpendicular to any plane of a model. Therefore, tool bit selection can play again an important role using 5-axe milling machines. In fact, it makes engraving of

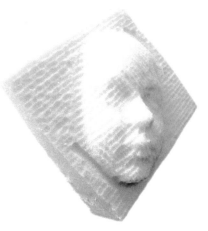

A relatively simple 3-axes cnc router has the capability to machine any 3d shape (as long as it is accessible with the toolbit). The cnc router does this by 'slicing' the model into small parallel sections that will be cut in shape one section after the next. Often a so called 'ball nose' tool bit is used for the final stage of this operation. The material is chipped away in various stages. First, a rough shape is created that takes away most of the material. Finally, the thinnest slices create the final image. This production method creates a rounded mechanical result. (Lower image)

The image on top shows the effect when the sculpted model is produced with tools working in all kind of directions (or axes). The visual effect is much more lively. (Sculpture of Francis Bacon by William Mather)

text on any shape or surface possible. Machine instruction for 5-axes machines is work for professionals. Designers can make their designs in 3d modelling software, but a professional has to make the translation for the tool paths of the 5-axes machine.

Specifying for rapid prototyping or 3d printing is more straight-forward. Designs have to made with modelling software and eventually converted to the 'stl' (stereo lithography) file format. This format is specially developed for the 'additive' technologies. There are a number of production methods to choose from, depending on the desired 'smoothness' of the surface, the colour, the strength, the production costs and the refinement of the detail. When the design is built from a liquid base material, in some cases a supporting frame has to be produced together with the workpiece to avoid collapse during its construction. The frame can be broken away from the model after the production is completed.

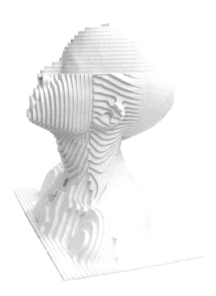

The Rolls Royces of the cnc router robots are capable of manufacturing practically everything that appears on a 3d digital file, as long as the tool bit can get there. The illustrations show the production process of gradually using finer toolbits (and toolpaths) towards the end result. To be able to deal with the heavy forces during production, these machines are very heavily built, huge and expensive. They are used in the automotive and aviation industry to create prototypes, dies and test models.
The end result will often have a smooth surface, which gives the model a bit of an 'automated' look. Results where the movements of the tool bits are still visible. look much more interesting from a sculpting point of view.

The types of base material to choose from are limited but when combined with all kinds of casting methods, a large variety of base materials can be used. Producing bigger objects tends to be costly, though, but is likely to drop in price over time when additive production will become widely used. Additive production is absolutely ideal to make a scale model of a 3d design. These scale models will give a far better impression about how the design will look in reality than any other way of visualisation. Never mind how exciting and persuading those other types of visualisation may be.

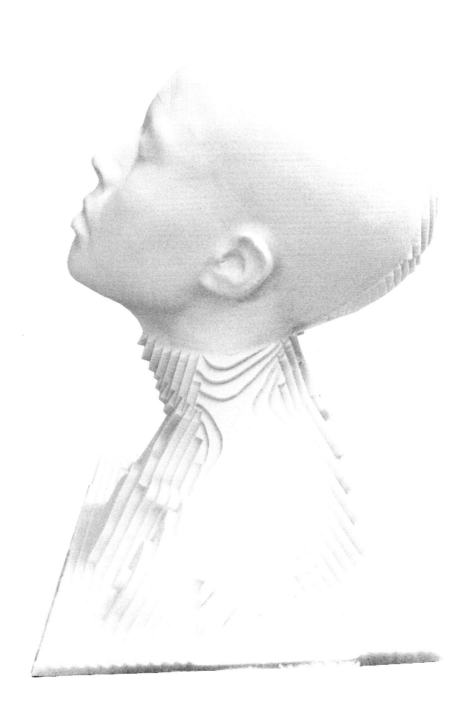

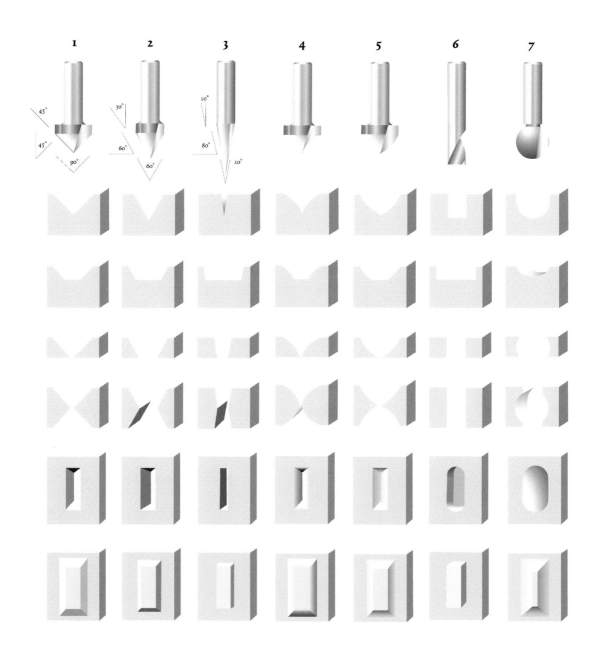

Cnc routers use tool bits to cut the material along a digital tool path. The tool bits can be divided into different types. The collection above shows a selection of these types and the effect they may have when cutting material in various ways.

The numbers 1–3 are v-carve tool bits, 4 and 5 are forming tool bits, number 6 is a so called end mill, and number 7 is ball shaped. The cut samples show the immense variety obtained. only by selecting a different tool bit to do the cut. Please bear in mind that the tool paths to make these samples is more or less identical.

5 Cnc routers and v-carving

Of all the machines that can be used for cnc manufacturing, the low-end 3-axes cnc routers are the most challenging and in some ways the most inspiring. The technology is relatively simple, the router is basically a traditional tool and can produce with low costs. The difference between a cnc milling machine and a router is not so much in the technical principles as it is in the way these types of machines are employed. Millers are used mostly used for making metal parts. They have more 'axes', work with solid materials, and are much more complicated to instruct. Routers are mostly used for wood or synthetic panel material. They are relatively simple machines and there is software available for these machines that allows a much wider audience to use this technology. Designing for a digital toolpath and combining this with the selection of a tool bit can make designing for cnc routers an exciting process.

The software
Designing for cnc routers can remain extremely simple. Cnc routers can work with outlines only. You can create these outlines with any drawing software and import the file created, or make the outlines with the cnc software that can also create outlines from imported halftone artwork. Cnc routers are often called 2d or 2.5 d machines because of their simplicity and their limited use of the three axes. An outline will be cut out of panel material at a predefined depth. So effectively, the machine only needs two axes to steer the tool bit.

The software allows the outlines to be used in different ways:
a. producing profiles, or cut lines.
This option has three variations:
— the tool path will be positioned on the centre of the outline.
— the edge of the cut will be on the outside of the outline.
— the edge of the cut will be on the inside of the outline.
b. producing pockets, or cut out the complete area between enclosed lines.

The three basic options of the cnc router: on top the simplest 2d routing where the outlines are followed and the cut depth is steady and preset. Thereunder is the v-carve cutting option. The software calculates automatically a centred toolpath with a split to each corner of all individual enclosed outlines. The cutting depth is automatically adjusted to respect the outlines. This option is sometimes called: 2.5d. The option at the bottom of the illustration shows a 'real' 3d cut. There are no outlines but a specific set of toolbits will follow the surfaces from the 3d digital file in small parallel moves.

c. producing so called v-carves.

This is a variety that requires the use of a pointy (v-shaped) tool bit. The software will create a centred toolpath in every enclosed shape but the centred toolpath will be split into two paths to lift the tool bit up to the edge of each sharp corner in the outline, in order to keep that corner sharp and not rounded. The depth of the cut is automatically adjusted to respect the silhouette of the outline. This results in a cut that looks much like the cuts of traditional letter carving in stone or wood.

d. producing drilled holes.

This option cuts a hole of the diameter chosen for the bit in the centre of objects.

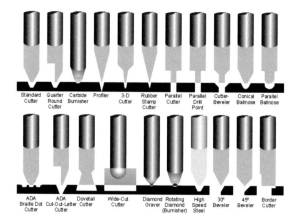

Tool bits come in endless varieties, matching the use for specific materials or specific applications. Even if the offer on the market is still not to your satisfaction, you can always order one with the shape you wish to have for a specific job.

The opposite page shows the variation of an identical toolpath using three different basic shapes of tool bits: a square one, a v-shaped one and one with a ball shaped ending. The two series on top show the engraved and the protruded version where the line of the outline is used as a single line. The two series at the bottom show. the result when the outline is used to make a pocket cut.

On the following two pages two more variations are shown. On the left page, a number of variations that can be made by combining the single line and the pocket cut.
The variations shown on the right page, can only be made with 3d modelling files.

As already mentioned in the previous chapter, cnc routers can also deal with 3d models in a large variety of formats. This is a different way of using the cnc router. It will change from a 2.5 d into a 3d machine. The tool paths and the tool bit selection are no longer defining the end result. One set of specific tool bits will cut out the final shape in incremental parallel cuts. Obviously, this a more complex way to produce. First, the designer needs to create a 3d file him/herself and manipulating this file is difficult. The cnc router software has the option to create 3d files or to use outlines or even photographs or other pictures as input to create 3d files. But these options should be used with caution, not all will create convincing results. Some of these options can best be considered as software gadgets.

There is a lot of different software around to be used for cnc routers. Some are proprietary for the machines, others are 'stand-alone' and can be used to instruct different cnc machines. All will have the option to create outlines themselves, manipulate (imported) outlines, create renderings of the end result and calculate the g-code on which the cnc machines will run. Software can have a steep learning curve when each step in the production and design process has lots of different options. And—be

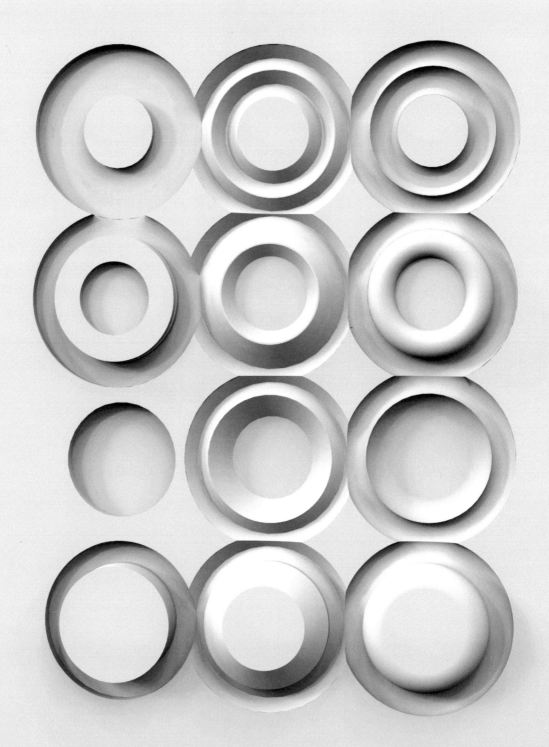

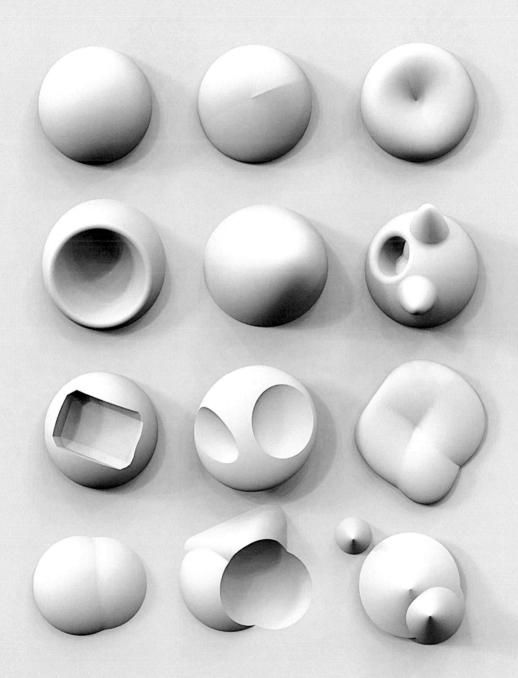

Rosettes, like all other decorative designs have experienced a revival thanks to the production options of cnc cutting machines. On these and the following pages, a number of varieties are shown that can make cnc routing even more exiting than just cutting decorations out of all kinds of material.

The illustrations on top show a series of 10 rosettes. The outlines of these rosettes are used as tool paths for the cnc router. The form variations to make with these outlines are infinite. The cnc software allows for different ways to use the outlines and the shape of the tool bits to use are boundless.

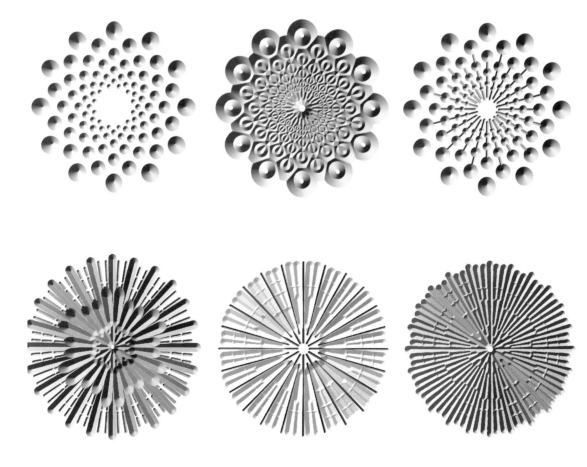

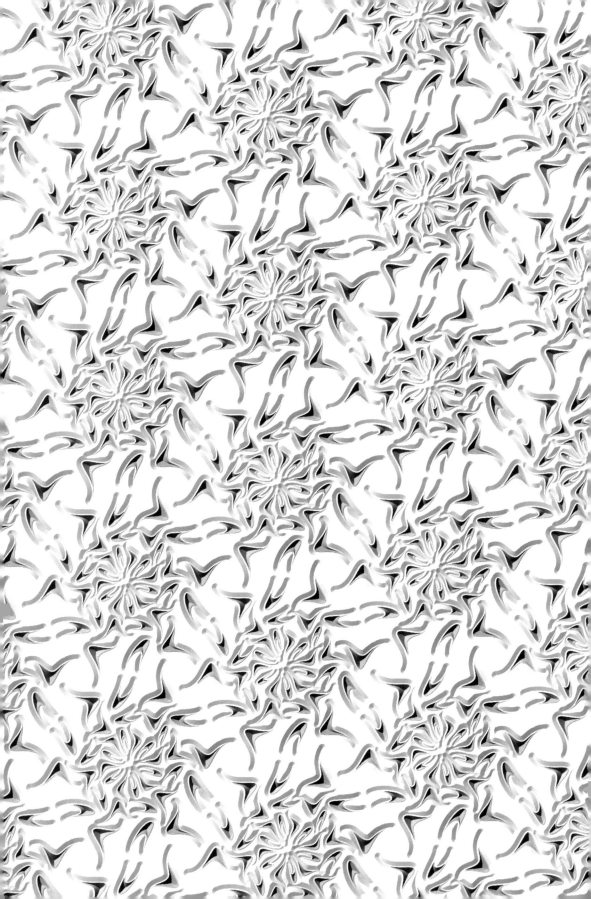

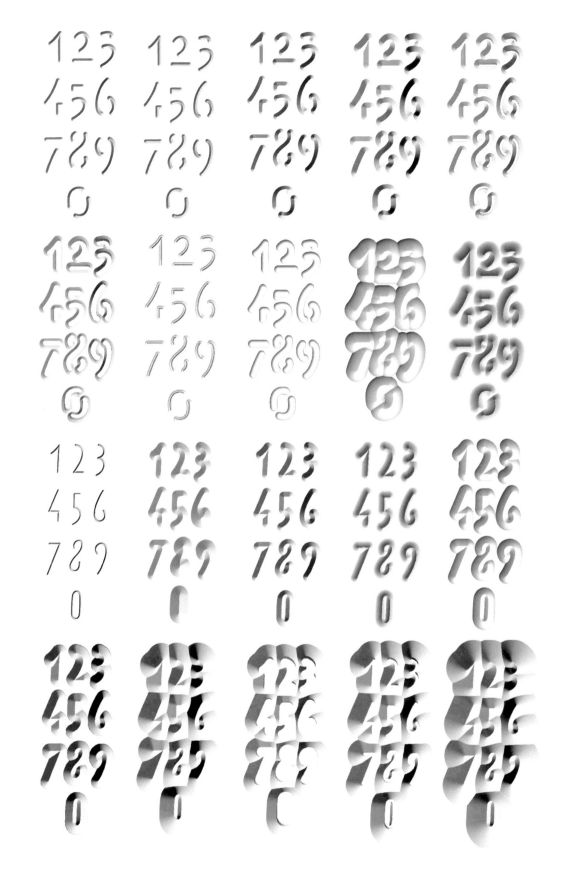

sure—these options only tend to grow over time. For designers it is interesting to know that some software can be tried out for a finite period. In these cases, often g-code cannot be produced but all the rest of the software can be used without restriction. This means that the designer can make renderings of designs before sending them into production. The author of this book has also been a grateful user of this trial software.

The above is an extremely concise description of the cnc software and it is mostly focussed on the design aspects of the software. A large part of the software deals with the technical aspects of carrying out the work, like specifying spindle speed, cut depth, tool bit movements and cut direction, etc. As with most software these days, a complete knowledge of all options for use is effectively only possible for people that work every day with the software.

The Tool Bits
A tool bit can give refinement and elegance to a cut. This ability makes cnc routers more interesting to work with than the plethora of different cnc cutters around. In general, there are a number of different tool bit types:
a. End mills are a group of rectangular shaped bits that are mostly used to clear pockets, or clear a layer from a surface to create protruding parts. End mills are also used to create the rough shapes for 3d models.
b. Ball noses are used for 3d modelling and texturing.
c. V-bits are used for v-carving that may give the impression of traditional hand carving. It can also be used to give shapes chamfered edges.
d. Form tools are used to give (panel) edges a specific and ornamental shape. Two traditional shapes in this category are the 'Ogee' and the 'Roundover'. Tool bits can be custom produced in almost any shape one desires.
e. Engraving bits are used for engraving in different materials, like wood, synthetic material, aluminum, brass and stone.
f. Specialst bits are for very specific jobs like engraving in glass.
g. Drills are used for the drilling option in the software.

The best typefaces to use
Cnc routers are excellent instruments to produce ornaments and textures. The most impressive results will be those made exclusively with the 2d and 2.5d modelling options of the machine. This is also by far the fastest and cheapest way to manufacture. V-carving a shape in a surface is easy and astonishingly fast. There are a number of ways by which tool paths can be created. To use a combination of these options will allow an immense freedom to create sparkling results. Regrettably, it is not possible to save files as 3d clipart for ornaments produced this way. The only option is to make one's file available to others, which can only be read by users having the same software. This limitation

The form variations for type produced with cnc routers are endless. This is specifically true when your font is a single line stencil font. This kind of font provides maximum of freedom, see pictures on the opposite page. The downside is that you have to create such a font yourself because those fonts are not offered anywhere. Hard to believe, but true. The options for form variations of available fonts are still substantial, but one has to be careful with using the cnc software. The above images show a decreasing quality when using the v-carve software option on different typefaces. The thin stroke connections of the sample on top create o.k. results, the quality decreases when the connections get thicker and will turn to Frankenstein mode with the thick connections in the sample at the bottom.

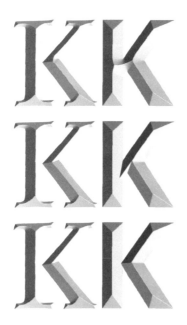

The image on top shows the letter cut created with v-carve software. The second image—an improved version—that cannot be produced with v-carve software. The third image shows that sometimes it is better to simply select a different typeface (the sans serif on the right) because very few typefaces will create acceptable results in v-carve.

A way to escape scrutiny of proper v-cuts, is to make outrageous cuts (pictures below) that avoid any reference to traditional letter carving.

means that ornaments are often produced using the 3d option of the machine, which is not the coolest way to use the machine, and also certainly not the fastest.

What counts for the production of ornaments and textures, counts also for the production of cnc type as well. Routers have a long history as producers of non-printed type. Engraving machines are routers, and have been around for centuries. Today, all of those machines are digital but they used to be mechanical tools. Typefaces were specifically designed for engraving machines. The fastest producing typefaces on these machines were the so called 'single line' typefaces. Each letter (glyph) consisted of one single tool path. These typefaces did not have differences in the thickness of the letter strokes. That was impossible to do with the mechanical machines, the tool bit followed only one line in a fixed depth to produce each letter. One had only the option to take another shaped tool bit or to make the overall cut depth higher or lower. All this could influence the thickness of the strokes or the visual effect of the cut depth. All letter strokes produced with a single line also had round ends, because of the method of production. The more complicated type designs for engraving machines had two or more (up to eight) tool paths within each letter. This way, the strokes could have thick and thin parts and more squarish corners for stroke ends. Designs for engraving type never really got the attention of the type designers working for print. Most type designs for engraving machines were made by technicians, or crafts people.

The quality of engraving fonts

At times, for some reason, established quality does not find a continuation in subsequent technologies. Engraving is one example. When it was a pure craft and letters were carved by hand with a basic tool (like a burin) into the surface, there were very skilled crafts people around who mastered a number of typefaces perfectly. That skill never made it to the engraving machines. Practically all engraving fonts around are sub-standard when judged as font designs. This circumstance is remarkable since letter carving of itself did have the attention of type designers. Letter carving was even seen as a basic skill best to be mastered by all type designers. A number of famous type designers were indeed fanatic letter carvers. The more surprising that the transition of hand carving to mechanical carving was never made. Engraving fonts are still used on cnc machines, because their basic design fits perfectly with the technology, as it always did. The Cnc software comes with a large collection of fonts (as with all software) but also with many engraving fonts. However, much caution is required to use these fonts, because the designs are mostly not refined and even the letter spacing is in most cases simply bad. Besides, today one can use every typeface on a digital cnc machine. Just convert your type into outlines and there you go. Yet the most sophisticated way to use type on a cnc machine

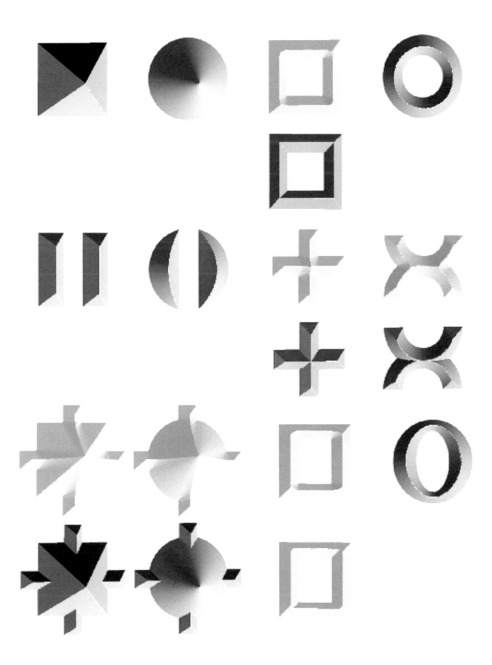

A sample overview of the rather strict limitations of use to accept when working with the v-carve software.
Shown are three horizontal rows of basic shapes. The light illustrations indicate the occasions where v-carve is incapable of creating flawless tool paths. Clearly visible, v-carve cannot even create properly the corners of a simple rectangular box shape. Matters get really out of hand when strokes or shapes are intersecting. In those cases, v-carve starts to produce all kinds of phantom shapes. In some cases, the flaws can be corrected by producing the shape in two separate runs. That option is shown in the picture underneath the light one. A rectangular box made with two different stroke thicknesses cannot be produced properly using v-carve.

Carving text in wood or stone has an influence on the lettershapes that are used. The specific constraints of applications always have their influence on typography. V-carving software allows for application on every typeface, because the software knows no quality restrictions. So we have to select our typefaces carefully. On the opposite page, is a sample of a typeface designed by the professional letter carver Tom Perkins. This typeface is not on the market. On the same page is the Trinité, a typeface designed for print by Bram den Does that has many of the same characteristics as the typical 'carver' typefaces.

On top of this page, is a collection overview of. the same foundry that sells the Trinité, the TEFF foundry.

At the bottom of the page, two samples of workarounds when using v-carve. The 'e' sample (Trinité) shows that the cursive version is a better choice for v-carving. By v-carving the bold 'e' in two runs, each with modified shapes of the 'e', the quality can be improved. The sample at the bottom is the Gill from Eric Gill. A famous typeface from a famous type designer who was also a highly skilled letter carver. What v-carve makes of his typeface would certainly make him turn in his grave. Repair is regrettably only an option for a few letters.

ABCDE
FGHIJ
KLMN
OPQR
STUV&
WXYZ

ABCDE
FGHIJ
KLMN
OPQR
STUV&
WXYZ

ABCDE
FGHIJ
KLMN
OPQR
STUV&
WXYZ

ABCDE
FGHIJ
KLMN
OPQR
STUV&
WXYZ

...of our being. Words a[re]
...oth our daily currency a[nd]
...ur most precious possessio[n]
...Words can change our hear[ts]
...nd minds. They can wou[nd]
...r heal, seduce or deter, mak[e]
...s laugh or cry, happy or sa[d]
...here is almost nothing wor[ds]
...nnot do. The written wor[d]
...n be kept forever, yet [its]
...eaning is elusive from th[e]
...oment they are used. Th[e]
...ly species that reads an[d]
...rites often sits when it doe[s]
...ords are our tools to gras[p]
...and create a new

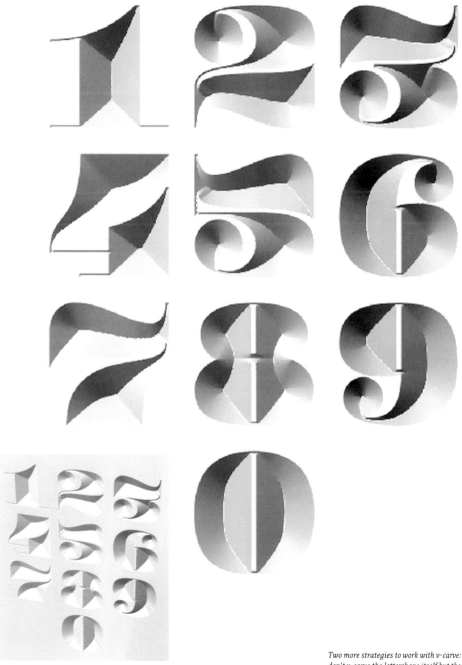

Two more strategies to work with v-carve: don't v-carve the lettershape itself but the shapes between the letters, image on the opposite page. Or, image on this page, pick an outrageous font, the free Pompido font in this case.

milk

oklahoma

news

april chapels

monkey

the Netherlands,

حين يكون مضمل يكف المغامظ عليه
الطائنة القادرة على الكتابة والقراءة
الكلمة هي أداتنا لاستيعاب واقعنا و
نستخدم الكلم للإدراك بيعمنا البعض.
حيها نعبر عن مشاعرنا من دون كلام.

CALLIGRAPHIC OR SCRIPT TYPEFACES ARE LIKELY TO PRODUCE THE BEST TOOL PATHS IN AUTOMATED V-CARVE.

Calligraphic or script typefaces are likely to produce the best tool paths in automated v-carve.

الخط أو الخطوط التقليدية هي على الأرجح الأفضل لخلق المسارات في النحت الآلي.

On this page an illustration that speaks for itself. On the opposite page, three typefaces that fit in the category of outrageous type designs; a style that is heavily influenced by lettering used for graffiti.
The typefaces shown are the Sutturah, the Klimax and the Tabboush.

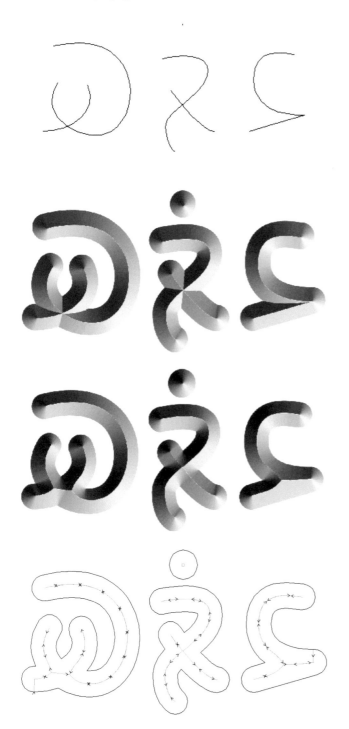

Engraving fonts
Engraving fonts
Engraving fonts
Engraving fonts
Engraving fonts
Engraving fonts
Engraving fonts
Engraving fonts
Engraving fonts
Engraving fonts
Engraving fonts
Engraving fonts
Engraving fonts
Engraving fonts
Engraving fonts
Engraving fonts

Aa Bb Cc Dd
Ee Ff Gg
Hh Ii Jj
Kk Ll Mm Nn
Oo Pp Qq Rr
Ss Tt Uu Vv
Ww Xx Yy Zz

is to use type that has a designed toolpath; not a toolpath calculated by the machine's software. As with producing ornaments, the software calculations may be impressive but all subtleties quintessential in the type design only get the attention they deserve when carefully designed and not calculated by a machine. That is just the way it is.

The problem with making real cnc type designs is that there are few authoring tools around that can create tool paths for fonts. All fonts on your computer need an outline to be made visible; one single line is not enough. (In fact, your computer will automatically create an outline when confronted with a single line font, which results in a complete form transformation.) Originally, single line fonts could be produced with font design authoring software, but this option was 'discontinued'. And cnc software is capable of a lot of things, but making font designs on them is a few bridges too far. So regrettably, the most ideal way to use fonts on cnc machines is not available and must wait until the professional type (design) community gets interested in the matter.

The wonders of v-carving

In the meantime, there is v-carving! V-carving is an interesting software invention that tries to mimic the traditional craft of letter carving. The nicest way to cut letters into a surface is to make a triangular shaped groove that follows the letter outlines and that permits square letter stroke endings by making a cut in the perpendicular direction of the stroke. The two cuts meet in a sloped corner that will end in the centre of the corner of each stroke. The software automatically creates a toolpath in the centre of each letter stroke that splits into two when coming close to the stroke end and the two toolpaths both end in each corner of the letter stroke. The software calculates these tool paths at an amazing speed. Also, text produced this way is executed in most surfaces extremely fast. Nevertheless, these niceties must be used with great care. The problem with this kind of software is that it always performs its task on whatever typeface or whatever other outlines you feed it. The software dutifully will calculate all tool paths and never says no, because of a likely bad end result. It leaves that judgement to us, so we must be careful when to use this interesting software option. Please bear in mind that the v-carving software is only capable of cutting simple shapes flawlessly.

By studying the tradition of carved lettering one discovers that the typefaces used for carving are likely to have a similar characteristic—although the variety of letter styles can be very large. This common characteristic is that it tends to follow the tradition of letterforms made with the calligraphic pen. All stroke variations and the way they meet seem to flow logically from the ink trace of letters written with a broad nibbed pen in a steady hand position. The only difference is that the carved version often has a stroke that gets broader at the end and/or also has small serifs. All are logical form consequences of the carving technique.

Script
Futura
Goudy
Roman
Balmoral
US Block
Block 2
Old English
Helvetica
AZURE
AUDREY
Baby Script
CONTEMPORARY
1234567890
ABCDEFGHIJKLMN
OPQRSTUVWXYZ
abcdefghijklmnop
qrstuvwxyz
! " & # ÷ - / \

Engraving fonts carry the most suitable instructions for the cnc routers. However, engraving fonts hardly ever got the attention of professional type designers. Engraving fonts now exclusively live on cnc software packages because the format is no longer supported by all companies involved in font distribution or production. As the fonts on these pages show, the engraving fonts available today are substandard in quality. Designs are outdated, letter, and word spacing are bad.

Engraving fonts used to be the only typefaces routers could work with. Today, cnc routers can work with any font. Nevertheless, the limitations of use are strict. A few Arabic letters shown on the left side of the opposite page show the ideal font design for a cnc router: a single line stencil font; but also the limitations of its effective use. This font design can only be saved in an outline format. The illustration shows how the cnc software creates from this outline a toolpath that changes the intentional single line toolpath (image on top) totally, resulting in bad quality (image at the bottom).

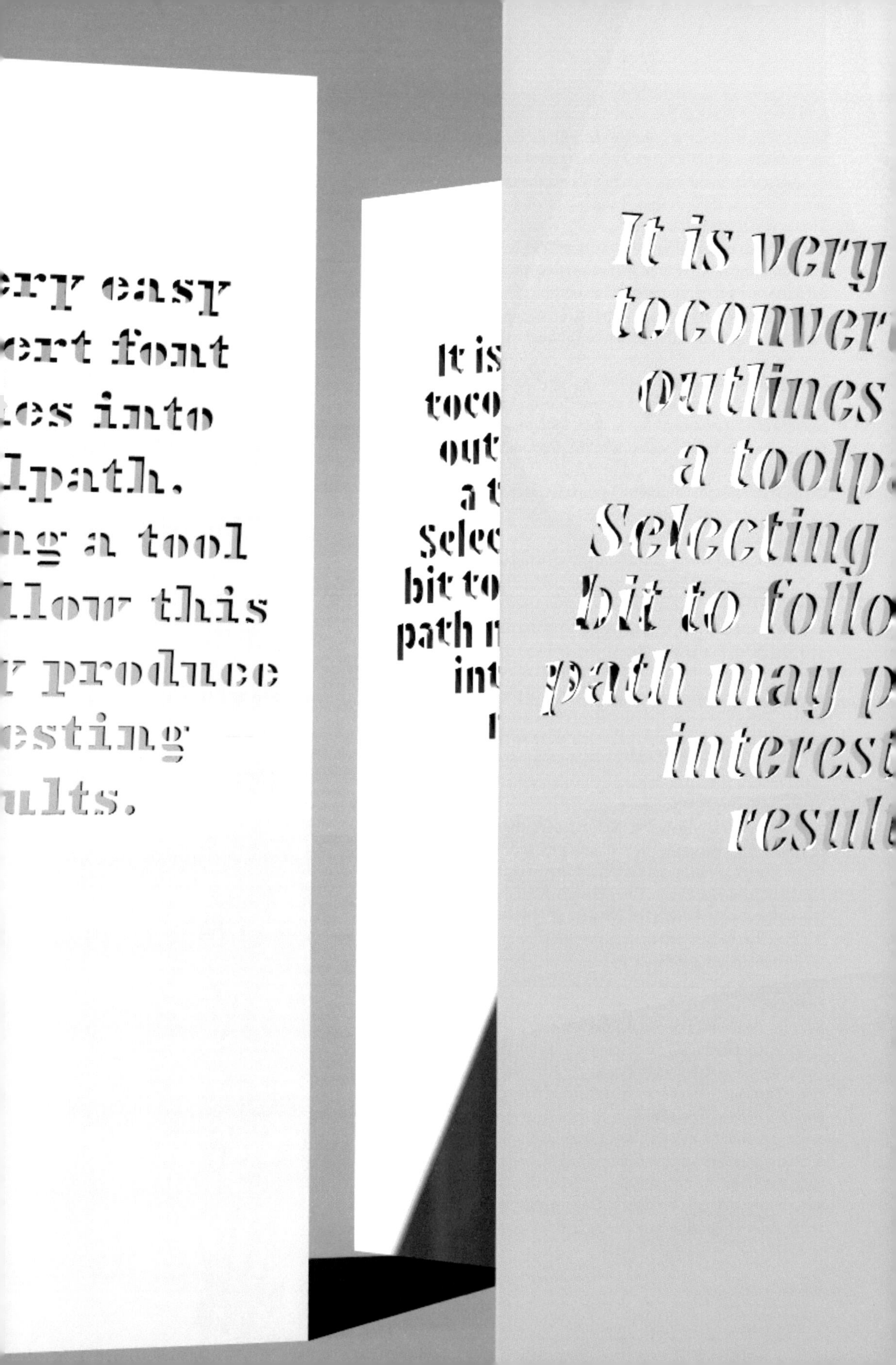

It is very
toconvert
outlines
a toolp
Selecting
bit to follo
path may p
interest
result

It is
toco
out
a t
selec
bit to
path m
int

ery easy
ert font
es into
lpath.
ng a tool
llow this
y produce
esting
ults.

v-carved stencil

v-carved stencil

v-carved stencil

V-CARVED STENCIL

v-carved
stencil

The correlation between hand carving and hand writing is hardly surprising. The first phase of carving letters out of a surface since Roman times was to paint the letters first with a flat brush on the surface before starting the carving.

Type designs made for print can also be designed following a writing tradition, but there are many fonts around that were designed against a totally different background, like optical corrections when used in very small sizes, or form corrections that create better results when used on a screen or in print, or type designs that just attempt to be outrageous or innovative in shape. All typefaces in the first category can be expected to have an automated v-carved version of reasonable quality. They are never going to reach hand carved quality level though. Typefaces from the second category are likely to make the v-carve software go berserk when creating the tool path of some letters. Don't be shocked when here and there Frankenstein versions of some letters will appear. The v-carve software is particularly bad in calculating the tool path of meeting strokes, especially when these strokes have a similar weight. That is why the best results will be obtained when the strokes have a large difference in width, as with script letters, or letters seemingly produced with a broad nibbed pen, or even better, letters that have no stroke connection at all (or very few), as with stencil letters.

Making textures and illustrations with the cnc router

This book emphasises cnc typography, but the options for texturing, ornamentation and illustration should also be mentioned, because these pictorial elements are constant companions of type. The cnc router software allows the input of lines, outlines and halftone images (next to 3d files in all kinds of format). All input can be converted into tool paths and ultimately into g-code to drive the cnc tool bit. This means that effectively all existing visual material can be used for texturing, ornamentation and illustration on the cnc machine.

However, the most exiting results will be realised by carefully interfering with the manufacturing process, by selecting the tool bit, the cut depth and—of course—the shape of the toolpath itself. The amount of varieties in output is endless. The possible variations in visual result, just by playing with the shape of the toolbits and the cut depth in relation to selection of specific parts of the illustration, are already immense. One basic file of outlines can lead to very different visual results. Illustrations in this book give an impression of the large varieties possible without changing the shape of any line in the file. The cnc software has the option not only to set a certain cut depth but also to instruct a gradual increase or decrease (or both) of selected toolpaths. This option adds to the already abundant options. The designer has basically the same options as the hand holding a burin or a chisel. The way the cnc tools are used are quite different though. In any case, using these options will provide the most exciting results. But, remember, the cnc router can also deal with all other sorts of input.

a b c d e f
g h i j k l m
n o p q r s t
u v w x y z
1 2 3 4 5
6 7 8 9 0

1932
UNITS
MOLDING
pachydermica

Stencil fonts have the largest spectrum of applications on cnc routers. On this pages and the previous double pages, are samples of some excellent stencil fonts: Eames Black Stencil, Bodoni Stencil, Pouchoir, Signed JNL, Puncho, Couteau Pro, Orly Stencil and Stencil.
On the opposite page and the following pages, samples of the endless universe of textures, ornaments and illustrations that can be produced with cnc routers.

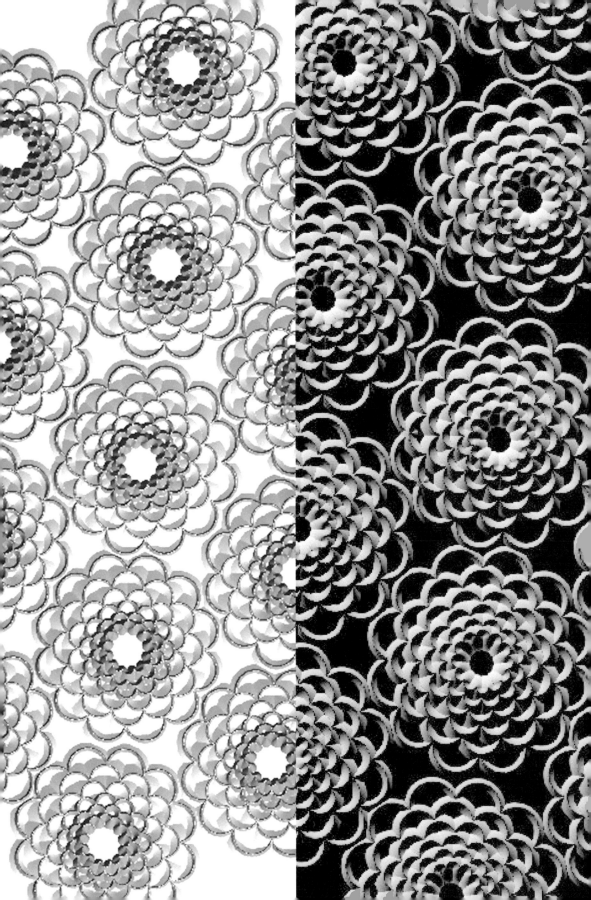

Listing the best ways to use the cnc router

Cnc routers can work with single lines or outlines as input to cut through material or to carve lines or volumes recessed in, or protruded from the surface. The shape of the line or the edges of the volumes will be influenced by the selection of the tool bit actually doing the cutting or carving. Stencils provide the option of being cut out completely from the material (without parts falling out) but can also be applied in a recessed or protruded version. Cnc router software has the option to do v-carving. The software automatically creates a toolpath that basically mimics the traditional way letters are carved in stone or wood. V-carving only works flawlessly for a number of very basic shapes. It cannot deal properly with the crossing or meeting of strokes. These characteristics lead to the following top five best applications:

1. The widest scope of use and the best quality result will be provided by using single line stencils (lines, shapes or fonts). Unfortunarely you have to make these types of stencils yourself because you cannot buy them anywhere. Maybe this is a blessing in disguise.

2. Outline stencils are the second best choice for use. They can be cut out completely or engraved. Even v-carving can be reasonably applied since stencil fonts have few strokes that meet. Stencil fonts and stencil clip art are for sale, some of very good quality.

3. Script, or classical 'Old Style' typefaces that still carry a strong calligraphic style are the best choice for v-carving, because the meeting of letter strokes is relatively thin, so the flaws of the software do not show so much.

4. Go mad with your designs. This way, all flaws in the v-carving software will disappear because they will look intentional.

5. The cnc router will function either as a precise cutting machine, or to make recessed or protruded volumes in a surface, or to make inlays of different materials. The cnc router will respect the precise shape of lines and outlines perfectly, only corners in the horizontal plane will need special attention.

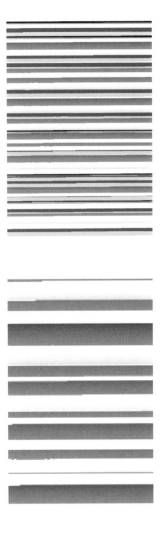

The tragedy of the low-end cnc routers

Permitting some sense of drama in expression, it can be said that there is a tragic aspect in the use of the simple cnc routers. The machines can produce beautiful and flawless stuff, but only when the machine is used to do the things which it is good at doing. And those are relatively simple things. When starting to make use of the most sophisticated parts of the software running on these machines, when using the 3d modelling and manufacturing option or even v-carving, the machine starts to expose its limitations. 3d models produced on a 3 axes machine—like most cnc routers—are simply inferior compared to what is possible to produce with a 5 axes machine. And the v-carve software for cnc routers is far from flawless.

However, the cnc 3d clipart became popular for use on low end cnc routers. That is sad because 3d clipart is almost always cheap and tacky stuff. This type of clipart hopes that by using 'classical'

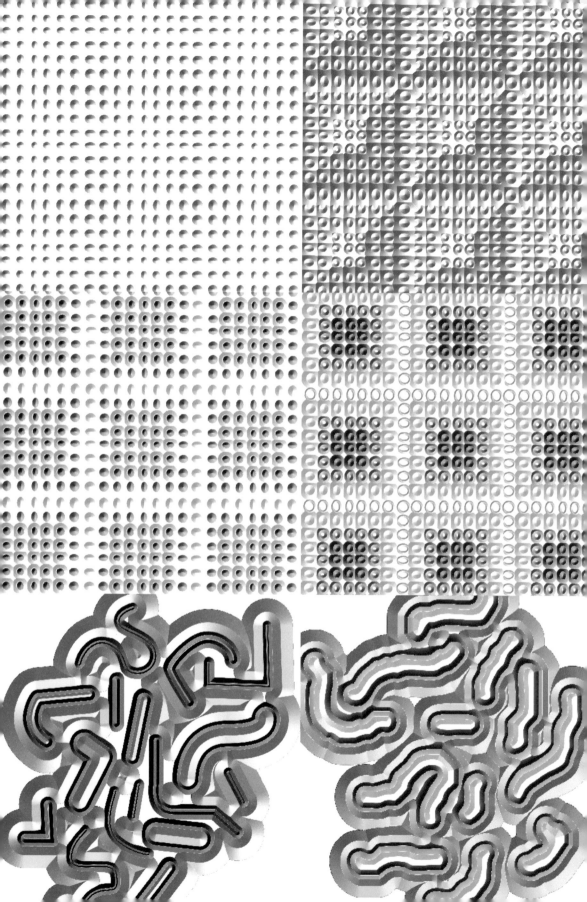

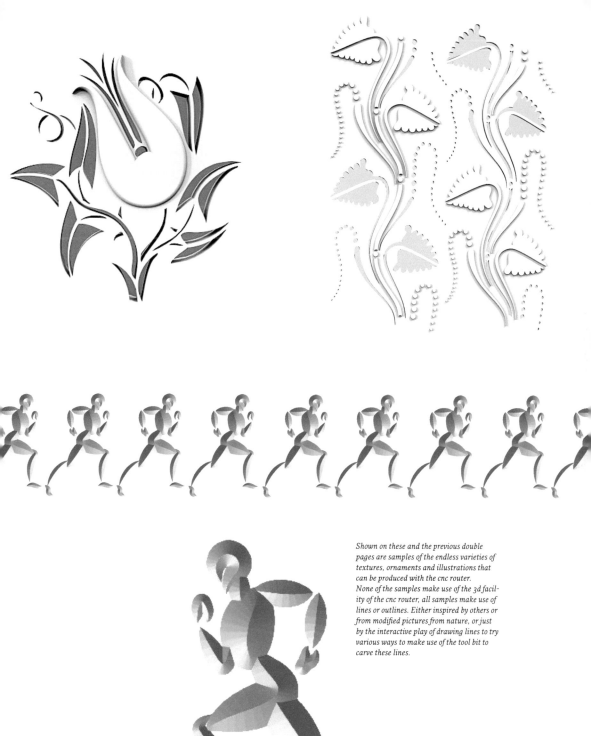

Shown on these and the previous double
pages are samples of the endless varieties of
textures, ornaments and illustrations that
can be produced with the cnc router.
None of the samples make use of the 3d facility of the cnc router, all samples make use of
lines or outlines. Either inspired by others or
from modified pictures from nature, or just
by the interactive play of drawing lines to try
various ways to make use of the tool bit to
carve these lines.

Visual artist Gordon Young often collaborates with the graphic designers group 'Why Not Associates'. Text and typography are an essential ingredient of his projects.

The texts he uses are not only to read, but sometimes also to sit on, climb into, or walk over. Gordon gave typography in the public domain many new and inspiring impulses.

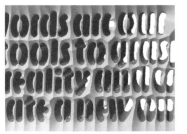

style themes, it will create a kind of professional distinction and a 'classy look'. Nothing could be further away from reality. This quest for superficial 'professionalism' is best to be skipped altogether. Metaphorically speaking, the result is likely to sound like Eliza Doolittle. A much better strategy is to explore the relatively simple production options. Bear in mind, that these options have great potential. With patience and perseverance the cnc router can produce wonderful stuff. In that sense, the difference between working with hand tools and digital ones is not that big. Easy solutions are hardly ever the best. It simply takes time to figure out how to make (out)lines, software options and tool bit selection work together in the most harmonious way. Regrettably, there is no other way to find out than following the hard route of 'trial and error'. It certainly helps that all cnc machines today have software that allows you to examine the results of your designs before you decide to produce the design in reality. It means that the trial and error period can take place for the most part behind your screen.

One single 'master' outline can be modelled in endless variations with a cnc router. The choice of the cutting depth and the selection of a specific single or a combination of tool bits makes this all possible.

Outlines, on their turn, can also be produced from almost any source: a scan, a picture, a photograph, a 'screen shot', a text file, a pencil scribble on paper, or a carefully produced outline in a drawing software. The options to create 3d stuff are almost frightening in number.

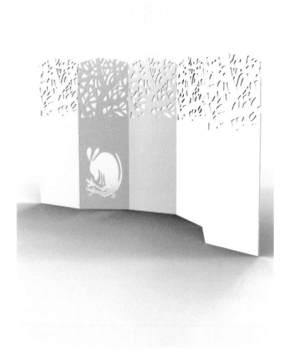

Illustrator Jeffrey Fisher created the graphics for this furniture series. His friend and colleague David Lancashire provided the kangaroo.

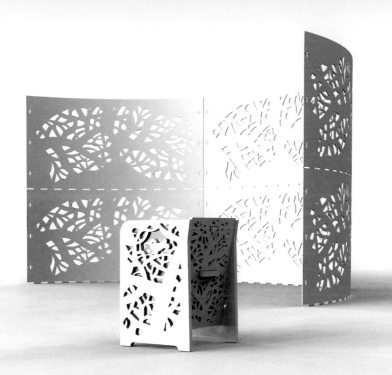

6 Digital issues and real problems

Our material and immaterial reality are becoming an ever finer mix. We have always been used to deal with both worlds; the real and the perceived one. Human perception and awareness are in material terms a complex system of tiny electric currents between our brain cells. That is how we deal with both the real and the un-real. At this level, it is much how it works in the digital universe, although in our case still much more complex. The material side of reality sets in when we get thirsty or hungry; then spill coffee over our laptop. In those cases, we may at first instance search for solutions to solve our problems, but in the end the only remedies are to be found in the material world.

The digital age created an environment where everything we can imagine, can in fact also be produced in reality. Only the laws of physics are our limits; no longer production technology. Today, cutters can cut through practically any material with digital precision. Cnc millers, routers and robots have a few constraints, but are amazingly capable of producing all what we can make visible on our computer screens. The latest 'additive' production technologies have effectively only limitations defined by the limits of what the physical world allows for things to exist and not collapse. What we can create and save in a 3d digital file can be produced. Interestingly, the latest development in production technology is in some ways for the designer also the simplest to deal with. The type of material you select for production by any additive technology will have some specific limitations but for the rest the designer can concentrate entirely on the imagination. So much freedom may easily be a curse in disguise.

Copyright issues

Our daily life has become a digitised one. We cross borders between the material and the digital reality so often each day that we do not notice the difference anymore. We capture the material world effortlessly with our digital (video) cameras or our 2d or

On the left page, experimental studies of 3d lettering the author carried out while studying at an art school in Amsterdam (1962). The studies were made by hand, first to produce a clay mold and thereafter cast in gypsum. This experimental way of lettering has remained exceptional. One of the few professional examples that is comparable to these experiments was created by the Norwegian designer Hermann Bongard in 1986 for 'Norges Bank', the central bank of Norway. On top of this page, we entered the digital era in the way we can make things these days. The image on top is taken from the internet as an example of the Islamic decorative canon. The second image shows the result of the automatic tracing of the image into outlines. The third image is the result of the outlines when carved with v-carving software.

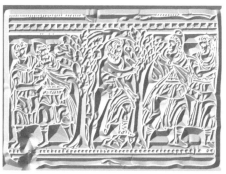

The internet is an inexhaustable source for images. They originate from all ages, contemporary and ancient ones. All this material can be transformed quite easily into 3d objects. The recipe is simple: grab the image from your screen and put it on your desktop, trace the image into outlines, and use the outlines for your cnc software. This software can also deal directly with halftone (pixelated) images. This easy trick needs respect for the copyright of others and often results in a product that looks like an easy trick. On this page and the opposite one, work from an unknown Etruscan and Chinese artist, portaits of Liz Taylor and an anonymus gentleman, the Arab calligraphers Wissam Shawkat, Ahmed Hilmi and his Western colleagues David Harris and Tashi Mannox.

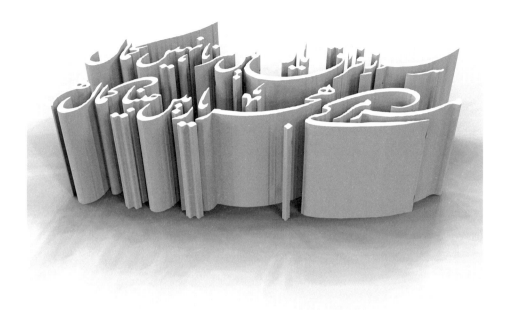

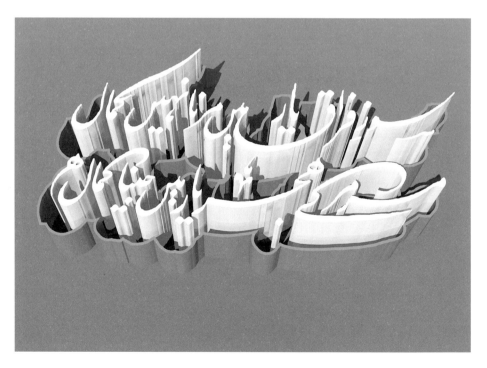

An Urdu poem taken from the web can be transformed into any kind of 3d object, even one that resembles a Japanese motorbike. What can be done with Urdu poems, can *be done with any other script. The turning page shows Chinese calligraphy by Harrison Xinshi Tu. The pages that follow show what may be the result when you take your digital*

camera on your visit to the Pompidou Museum in Paris. Just take a few shots of your favorite pictoral icons hanging there and give them a second life in, for instance, specially produced furniture items with the help of a cnc router. Many thanks to Giacometti, Picasso, Malevich, Matisse, Jeffrey Fisher and David Lancaster.

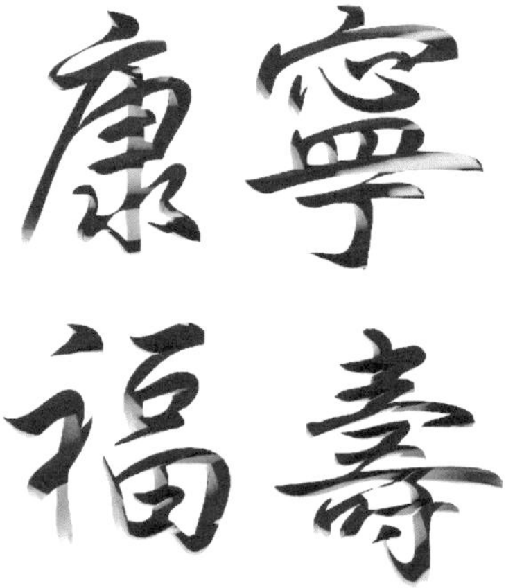

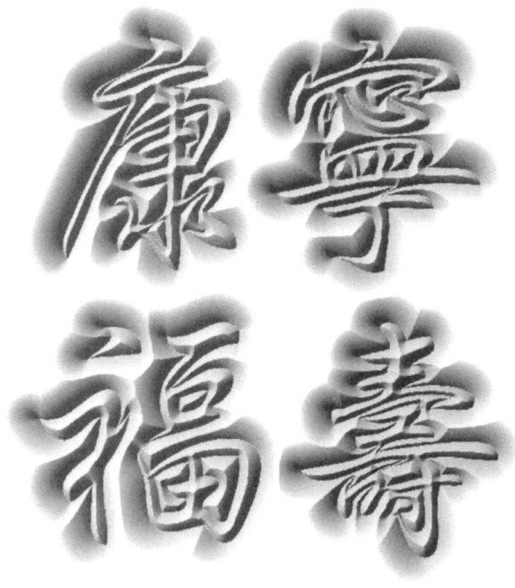

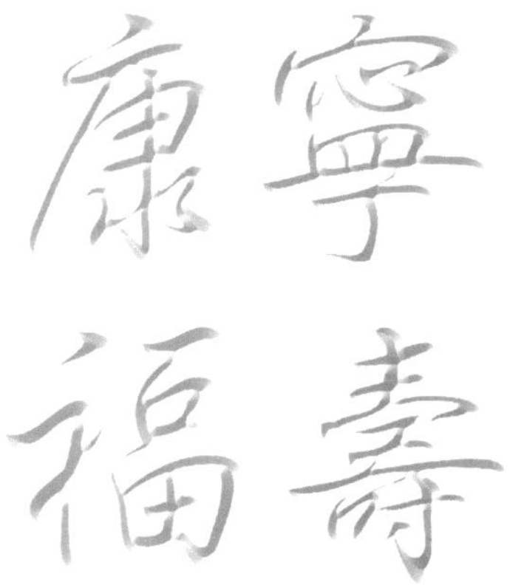

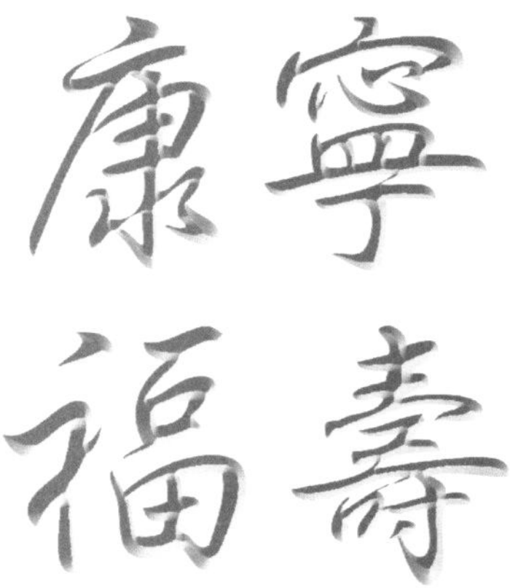

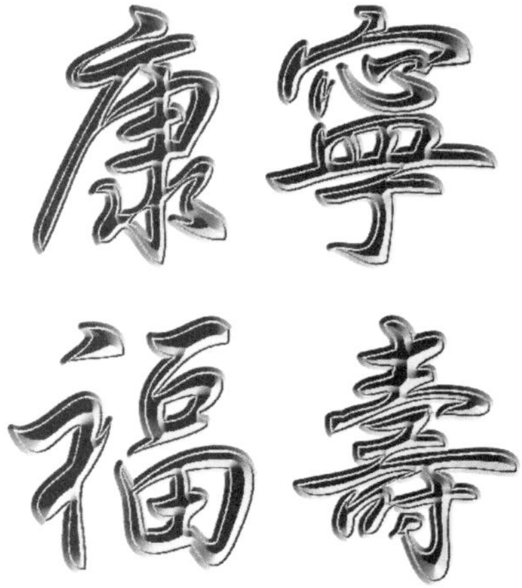

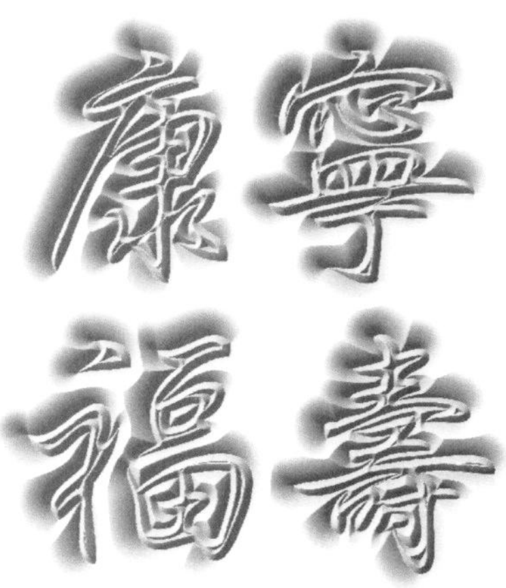

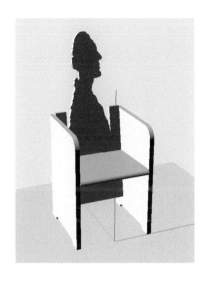

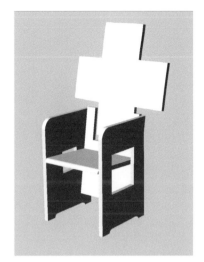

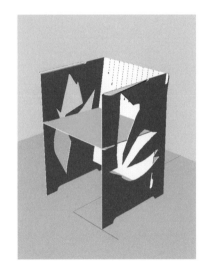

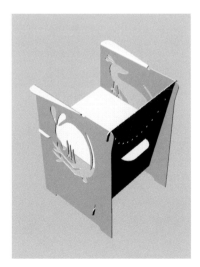

3d scanners and convert all this to our 'own' digital files within seconds. We observe the world more and more through the windows created by the digital media. We consume information and communicate with each other digitally. The internet has become everyone's ultimate source of information for almost every aspect of our lives, privately and professionally. And to 'possess' the information appearing on our screens could not be easier. Just drag the file to your desktop or make a screen shot. Thereafter, the images are 'yours' and you can do with them whatever you please. Armies of lawyers and many court cases have already dealt with all the legal implications of our new digital Pandora's box. The effective outcome is that copyright remains for the time being basically as it was, only we have a large freedom to do what we please within the confinement of the walls of our homes. Once we go public with our interventions, we have to obey the rights of those who created—not to be mixed up with physical ownership—the original works. It is in the interest of everyone to keep it that way. Borders of creative ownership are not always well defined. Even the most creative artists often know precisely who influenced their work. We get inspired by what others do. 'Sampling' and 'citations' have become accepted forms of re-creation. One of the most interesting new developments in the digital era have been the spontaneous creations of 'open source' networks. Extremely sophisticated knowledge banks in software are created on a voluntary basis and can be used for free by an undefined and rotating group of highly motivated and knowledgeable individuals. This is a very uplifting aspect of our human capabilities, especially when set against the background of our apparent inability to deal collectively properly and respectfully with our own natural habitat.

The digital era has brought some changes in how we deal with copyright, it brought us new concepts like the creative commons, which means that everything produced under this seal maybe used freely by others as long as the original creators are mentioned and their work is not violated. Slavish copying and counterfeiting are obviously not allowed, the last is even protected by criminal law.

In the meantime, it has become extremely simple to copy and recreate everything that surrounds us—whether it is created by others or by divine intervention. With a 3d scanner we create a 3d file that can reproduce the scanned object with little effort. So, everything of 'Nature's own creation' can be reproduced in any kind of material without copyright worries. The Almighty does not claim copyright so far, although some religions forbid the reproduction of nature's creation by humans. Almost everyone owns a 2d scanner, a computer with internet connection and a digital camera. All these instruments can make high quality digital files within seconds of everything we wish to capture. These files can be manipulated simply and for instance be converted into outlines that can be fed to our cnc production machines. The

The geometric patterns and Arabesque decorations have an extremely rich tradition in the so-called Islamic countries. For centuries, craftspeople and calligraphers have built an immense collection of ever more refined samples that can be found everywhere, much of it as copyright free artwork. Cnc machines can reproduce this material almost perfecly and can make endless variations with one set of outlines.

The number of sources available to find 'Islamic Patterns, (Sacred) Geometry or (simply) Decoration' is huge. There are many books published about the subject. Some carry CDs with copyright free samples. Of course, the internet is also an inexhaustible source. Through this medium one can download for free the 'Taprats' software, originally designed and written by Craig S. Kaplan, based on the tradition of geometric tiling. This software makes it easy to design pefectly precise geometric patterns which can be used effortlessly for cnc production.

The following pages show only a few variations of the endless variety to be found everywhere and easy to customise. This abundant availability does not preclude quality; results can be stunning.

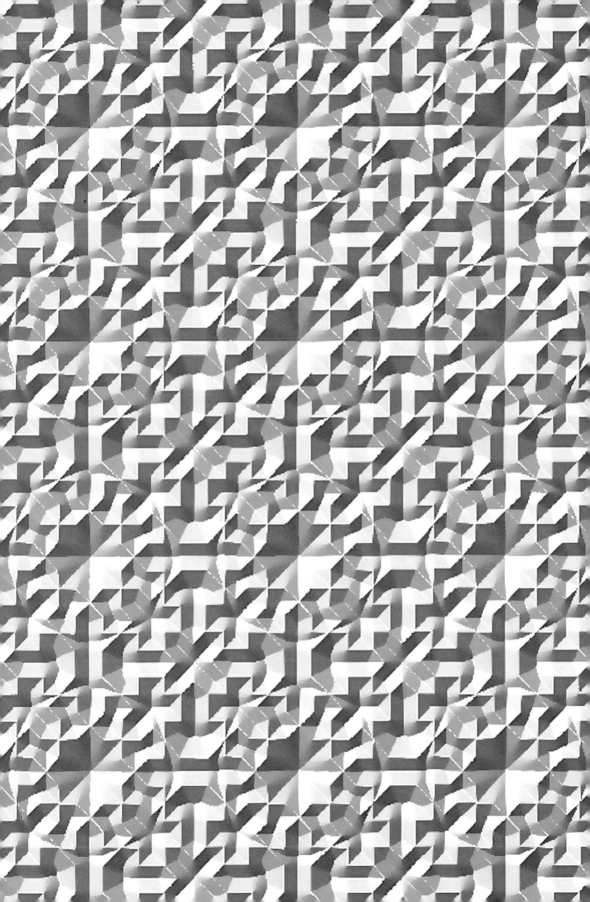

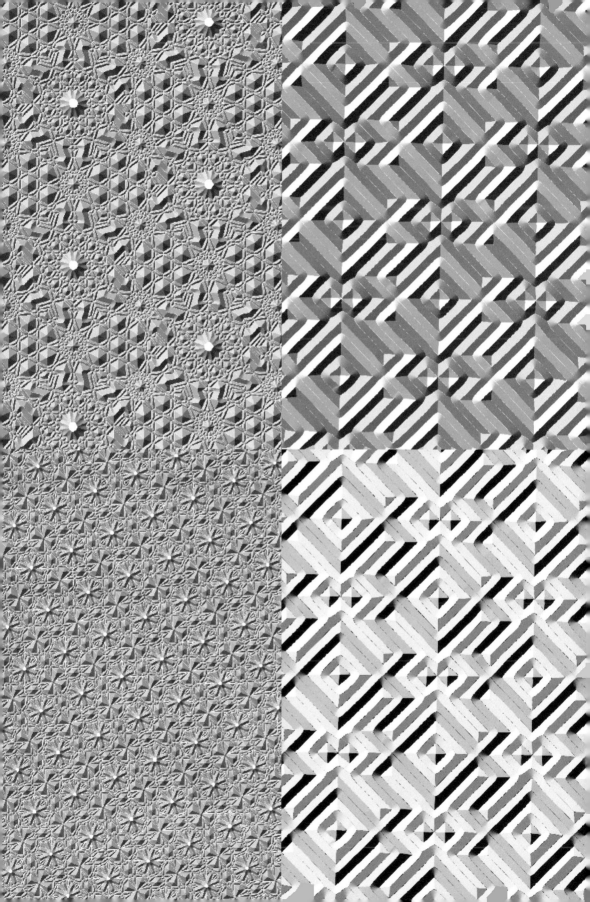

Do not fear that the only available options to create patterns will be from Arab descent. Western type designers also have discovered ways to produce ornamentation digitally and allowing for easy customisation. Their source of inspiration is often the graphic embellishments used for printed matter in the old days.

The samples on these and the two following pages are created with a font called 'Cadence' designed by Jonathan Perez. The font comes in three files, costs € 75,– and allows you to create enough variations to easily redecorate the complete Chateau de Versailles.

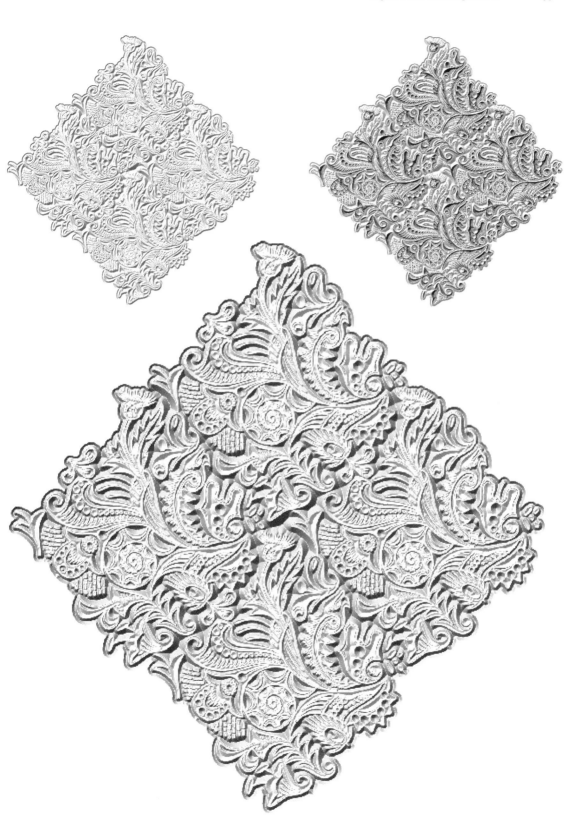

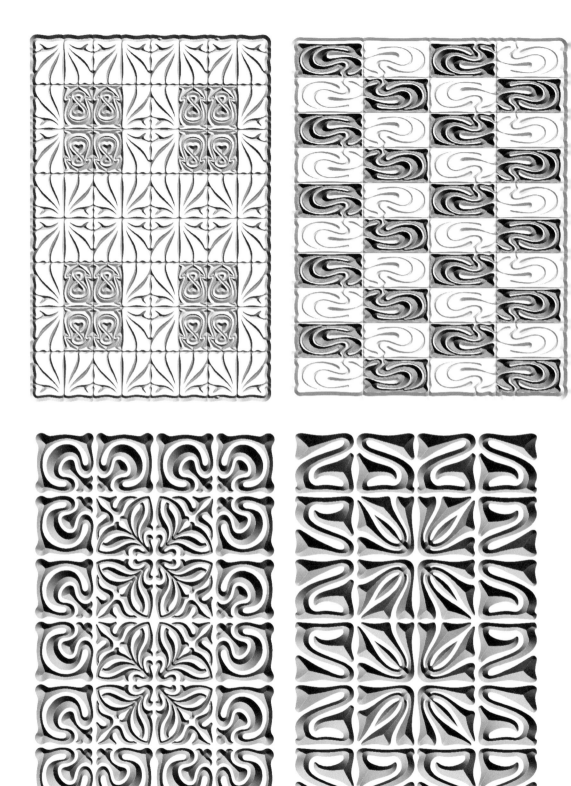

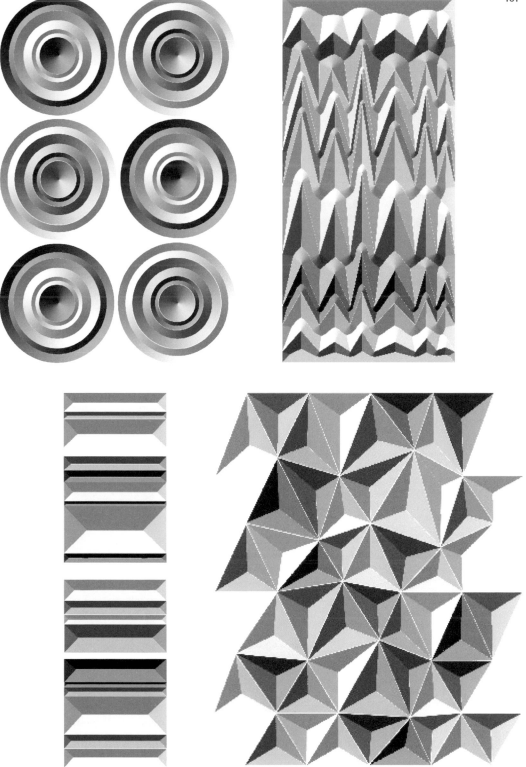

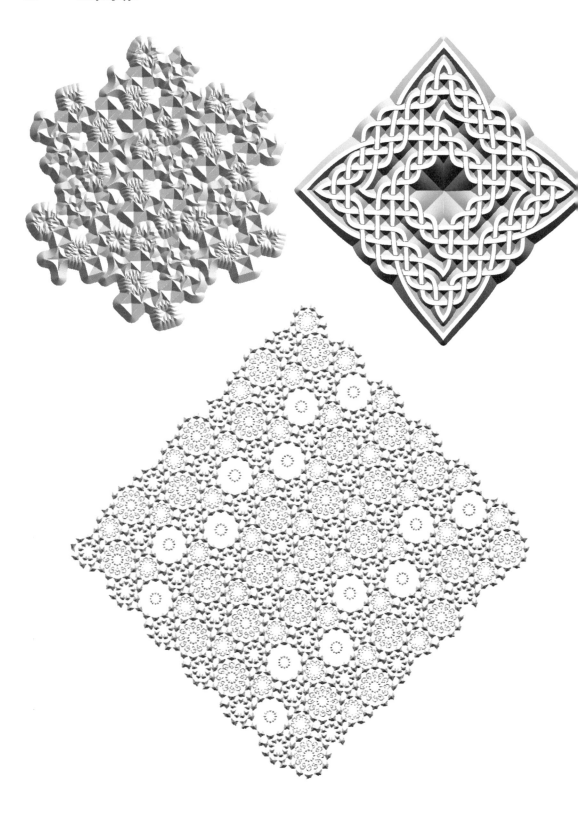

temptations to make creative shortcuts are big and the options to reproduce are perplexingly simple and fast.

Cnc software (and some 3d modelling software) has made it particularly simple to work with 2d files and use these files to create 3d objects. In some cases it works very well. Not in all instances, digital conversions of photos to 3d files are mechanical tricks, creating unimpressive results. But outstanding art pieces can be scanned and transferred into a 3d object that may look stunning. The author of this book will show samples of how this transformation looks. However, the real purpose of this publication is to make designers and visual artists traditionally working in 2d enthusiastic about using the simple options to produce their work in 3d. Product designers as well as animation artists already know how to deal with 3d modelling software. Visual artists, typographers, type designers and graphic designers should also discover the wonders of the 3d universe.

Conversion problems between 2D and 3d file formats

From the outset, there has been a more or less strict division between software development for the 2d world of print and digital media and the software development for the 3d world of engineering, architecture and product design. (With the animation software as a special section in the 3d world). Cnc routers have been used for a long time to produce typography and illustrations for signage, display and advertising purposes. At the introduction of cnc machines, the 2d artwork was simply traced by hand to create a file that could be used for cnc machines. That method was tricky, because is was not always made clear to the designers in 2d that the 'conversion' was done this way and at times, the tracing was done pretty sloppily. Typographic quality hangs on the quality of the details. There is no room for sloppy tracing. Today, tracing by hand is unlikely to happen, although it is advisable to remain diligent. Problems still may occur when files made with a drawing software are imported to a 3d environment.

These problems stem from the different way the outlines are made; drawing software uses 'splines' to define curves and 3d software often still works with a combination of straight lines and circle segments. Next, the level of precision between 2d and 3d differs. Software dealing with images for print and digital media accept pretty 'dirty' files, meaning files where not all lines of an outline are effectively connected, anchors (nodes) are put on top of each other and some parts of the outlines as well. Sometimes, a mix of bitmap and vector information are put together into the same drawing file. All these issues may cause digestion problems when imported to 3d software which is much more precise and can deal much less easily with imperfect 'dirty' input.

These types of conversion problems come and go, each version of each software has its specific problems and by googling your problem some advice is likely to come to rescue and help you to

The number of sources to choose from to acquire inspiring outlines to use for cnc routers is almost limitless. In fact, there is an abundance of material available for free, or at very little cost, in every historical and regional style and for every taste. There is absolutely no need to turn to 3d clip art. On the previous double page on the left, a few samples in the 'Art Deco' style using the font Heraut AS Ornaments designed by Andreas Seidel, on the right, we entered—style wise— the era of Modernism. Just limit yourself to simple geometric forms of your own design and use the v-carve option with v-carving tool bits in three different angles (60, 90 and 120 degrees). Using this recipy, the results will be flawless and impressive. Do not worry, trust your own imagination, you cannot go wrong.

On the opposite page, samples with outlines from three basicly different sources: the internet, your own design (funky geometry designed by the author) and from another designer: Farah Behbehani.
On top, fine artists should not be overlooked as a potential source. A cnc translation of an art piece made by Cathérine Zask.

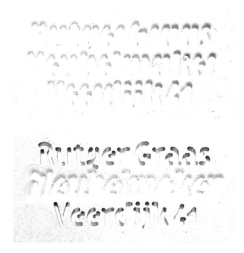

solve your specific problem. In general, there are a few things one can do to prepare your drawing or illustrator file in the best way to perform a smooth conversion.

a. Check your illustrator file for double outlines. The impressive 'live trace' option often created a positive and a negative outline on top of each other. One has to be removed.

b. Run a script—downloadable from the internet for free—that 'merges' anchors that are—invisibly—put over each other.

c. Another script will also close tiny 'holes' in your outlines.

d. To avoid bitmap information being part of your Illustrator file, save all the outlines in your drawings in the finest line thickness available and keep all outlines empty. You can check whether your file carries bitmap information by checking its size. Vector files are by definition small in size.

Some 3d software has the option to check and repair imported vector files themselves. In those cases, one can make the vector file cnc ready in a later stage.

3d software does not easily consume outlines made from text. These files become easily too heavy or too complex for the 3d software to deal with. One reason is that the conversion 'make outlines' from the text made with your Illustrator software does not produce the outline used in the font software. The Illustrator software 'recreates' the outlines. And outlines for 2d are by definition 'sloppy' compared to 3d files. That is why it is often better to use the 3d software to make texts because in that case the 'original' outlines of the font will be preserved and less likely cause any problems. Nevertheless, expect text to be much more cumbersome when used with a 3d software.

Basic material selection
The amount of different basic material to choose from today when producing something is large. Especially exploring the ever expanding collection of synthetic (panel) material is worth the effort. However, each type of synthetic material needs specific ways of machining. Do not expect your cnc router to easily deal with all kinds of different materials. They often need special tool bits and specific feed, and spindle speeds. Use cutters if you want to produce problem free work. Water-jet cutters will cut through most materials without any hassle, even wood. But, one has to accept that water jet cutters are more expensive to use than cnc routers and they can cut only straight through material. There is not the option to form the groove or the edge as with cnc routers. Although the most advanced laser, and waterjet cutters around can also engrave and cut under different angles. The cutting equipment available is so diverse that it is relatively easy to find the right combination of material, required quantities and price. The basic material selection at the other end of the spectrum—for additive production technologies—is also pretty straightforward. Price, required strength and precision are the considerations that makes material selection relatively easy.

Illustrations on the opposite page show the problems that may arise when using synthetic materials with the cnc router. The sample on top shows the result when using MDF panel material. A straight cut normally works well, but the core of MDF has a looser structure than the surface and that shows when using modeling tool bits.
The second image shows that nylon—a nice looking and strong material—needs special tool bits to create clean edges.
The same is true for the economic pp (polypropylene) material shown underneath.

For cnc routing, the spectrum to choose from is somewhat smaller. Most wood (panel) material can be used, but wood splintering can be a nasty complication when working with this natural product. For this reason beech and bamboo, for instance, are wood favourites. MDF (Medium Density Fibre) panels are often used as basic material for cnc routers. This material is cheap and suitable. The limitation is that profiling edges is not very possible since the core of the material is not as dense as its surface. MDF also needs coating and coating MDF is a relatively costly operation.

'Solid Surface', is a man-made material usually composed of marble dust, bauxite, acrylic or polyester resins. It is available in thickness of 3, 6, 9, 12 and 18 mm. Well known brand names are 'Corian' and 'Hi-Macs'. This material is expensive but it has excellent qualities for tooling with cnc routers.

A cheaper alternative are the 'Compact Laminates'. This product has a core of paper layers immersed in phenolic resin and a decorative cover layer on top and bottom of melamine pressed together under high temperature and pressure. Traditionally, this product has a brown or black core and thin decorative layers in an endless variety of structures and colours. Today, varieties with a multi coloured core or a solid (same colour as surfaces) core can also be found. In principle, panel thickness can be ordered on demand. Standard thickness are 6, 9, 12, 16 and 18 mm.

Cnc routing is an economic production option and it has a lot of modelling choices, but it comes at the price of quite a few limitations for the basic material to use. All these limitations will basically disappear when using the large array of specific cutters.

On the left page, cnc routing samples in various materials. On top one of the oldest synthetic materials: pvc. It is a tough and durable material, but it will need special attention to get smooth cuts. The second sample, shows the result when using compact laminates, a hard surfaced material used for table tops and outdoors signage panels. The last sample, a solid surface material, is ideal for cnc routing. The cuts will be smooth and pefect. The only downside is that your toolbits will wear out a bit faster.

Choosing the right cutting speed when using a cnc router is essential to create a smooth cut. Modelling tool bits cause a basic problem in this respect, because they will never have the same cutting speed over the full length of the cut. The illustrations show how a steady machine speed A translates in a slower speed at point B and a much higher at point C. These inevitable differences in speed are the major reason for the problems of creating smooth cuts, when cutting synthetic materials.

ABCDEFGHIJKLM
NOPQRSTUVWXYZ
1234567890
ABCDEFGHIJKLM
NOPQRSTUVWXYZ
1234567890

7 Fonts designed for 3d applications

The number of fonts available today is overwhelming. Every day, hundreds of new fonts are added to the already gargantuan collection. Nevertheless, do not expect a complete absence of 'blank spots' in the fonts universe. There are many, because type designers tend to be a rather conventional lot. Most of them will readily accept the borders of a traditional professional playing field for their crafty art and will concentrate almost entirely on the minutia of character shapes or the technology of font production. Without a doubt, details matter a lot in type design and typography, but there are many human activities where fonts are used that are practically untouched by professional type designers.

On the opposite page, a sample of the 'Pyramide'™ font, designed by the author using a modelling software. Hopefully the design will stimulate the interest of professional type designers for developing 3d fonts. The Pyramide™ is also available for the Arabic script.

Almost 100% of all type design is made to be applied for 'the media' which means for text appearing on screen and/or in print. The whole world of 3d is effectively neglected. There have been some minor 3d type design experiments and initiatives here and there, but there are close to no fonts on the market that are specifically designed for 3d realisation. A rather meagre result especially when set against the mountains of fonts available for media use. It is about time to change this situation.

3d monospaced fonts
Carving and engraving are the traditional ways to produce 3d typography. These activities have largely stayed firmly within the hands of skilled crafts people and/or never really got the interest of professional type designers or type foundries to produce carving or engraving in an industrial way. Over time, exquisite examples of architectural facade lettering have been produced, especially during the twenties and the thirties. But these were all one-offs, also produced with an indispensable contribution of craft skills. Industrial production in this segment never took off, other than in often depressing series of loose 3d letters in traditional shapes. Manufactured for cheap, do-it-yourself lettering. These were low cost and low risk business initiatives to keep

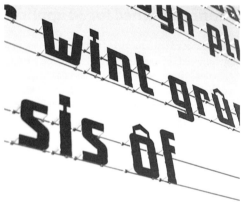

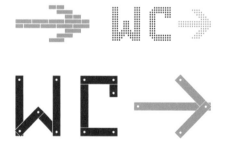

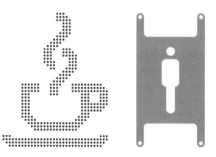

The Dutch graphic designer René Knip collaborated with type designer Janno Hahn to create a type collection specifically for use in 3d. Their initiative is quite unique. The type collection is shown and offered through www. arktype.nl

Illustration opposite page: most stencil fonts have too tiny separations to be used as real stencils. The FP Palina (designed by Morten Rostgaard Olsen and Ole Søndergaard) is a rare exception that can be used wonderfully for 3d applications.

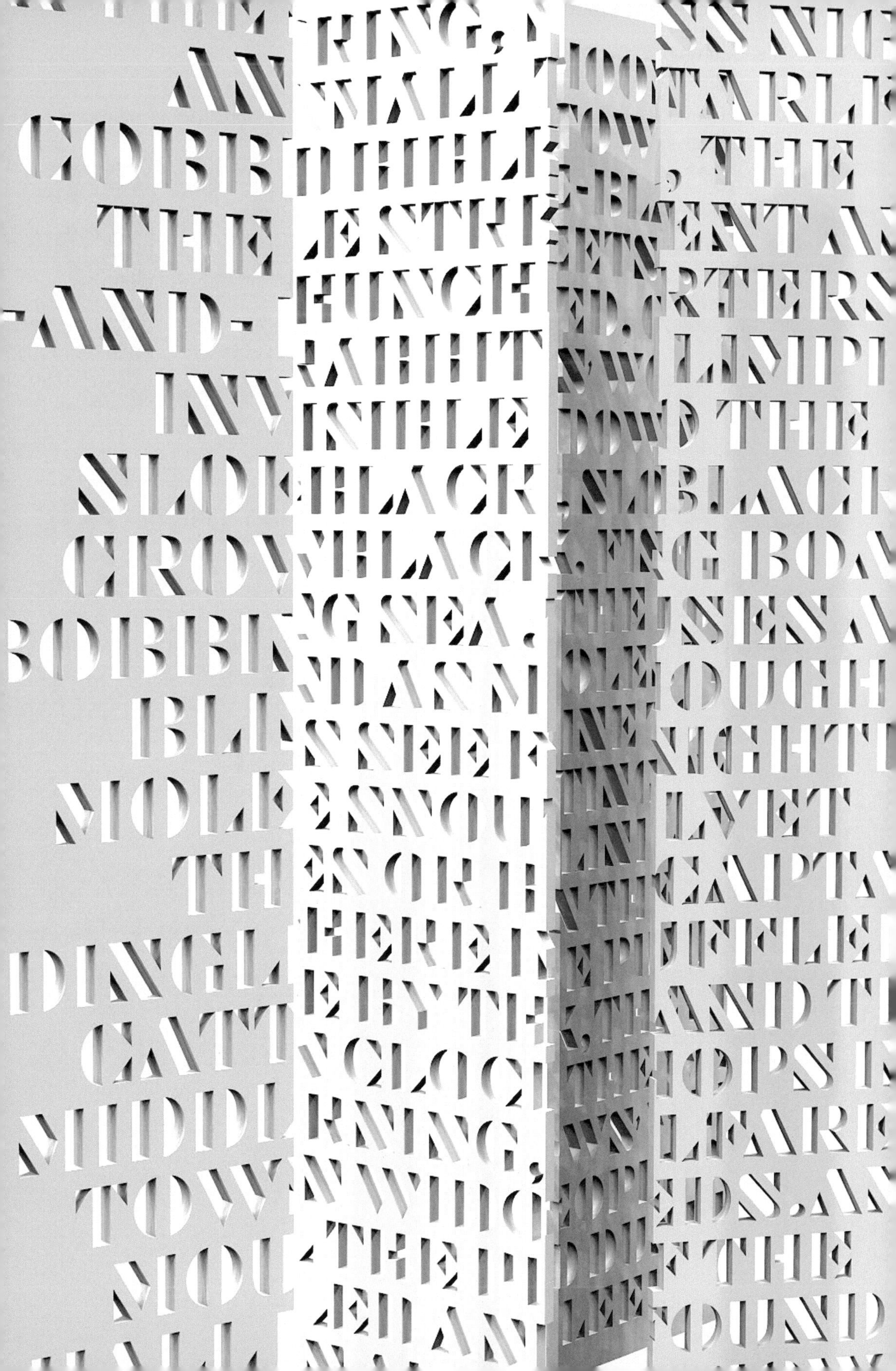

AN
COBB
THE
-AND-
INV
SLO
CROW
BOBBIN
BLI
MOLE
TH
DINGL
CATT
MIDDL
TOW
MOU

RING,
WALL
HILE
STRI
HUNCH
RABBIT
ISIBLE
BLACK
BLACK
G SEA.
MAS N
S SEE F
S NOU
S OR B
HERE I
E BY TH
CLOCI
RNING
N WHO
THE H
ED AN

HOO
OW
-BL
ETS
ED.
DOW
LO BLACK
FING
E US
OLE
NE
NI
TH
TH
OD I
LEE

S NIC
TARLE
, THE
NT AN
RTERS
LIMPI
THE
BLACK
BOA
SES A
OUGH
NIGHTI
LVET
CAPTA
UFFLE
AND T
OPS I
LFARI
DS, AN
THE
OUND

##$%&'()*+,-./01
23456789:;?·A
BCDEFGHIJKLM
NOPQRSTUVWX
YZ'

#$%&'()*+,-./01
23456789:;?·A
BCDEFGHIJKLM
NOPQRSTUVWX
YZ'

##$%&'()*+,-./01
23456789:;?·A
BCDEFGHIJKLM
NOPQRSTUVWX
YZ'

##$%&'()*+,-./01
23456789:;?·A
BCDEFGHIJKLM
NOPQRSTUVWX
YZ'

##$%&'()*+,-./01
23456789:;?·A
BCDEFGHIJKLM
NOPQRSTUVWX
YZ'

the factory busy during quiet periods. The world of 3d lettering has obviously not been entirely absent or poor in quality, some manufacturers of neon (boxed) loose letters reached a very high professional level with their products, but on average quality of lettering in the built environment tended to be below standard. Industrially produced 3d lettering products (or fonts) are extremely rare. A recent initiative by the Dutch graphic designer, René Knip (www.arktype.nl) is an exception. More type designers and type foundries should feel attracted to this less overly grazed and fresh new field of type design. The author of this book also made a contribution with his design for the 'Pyramid' font. The font is designed using only 3d software. No outlines of this font are available, although it would be interesting to produce a two layer version of the font especially for cnc v-carving. (All fonts used for v-carving should be designed in two layers to produce stroke connections properly).The idea for the Pyramid font stems from a design proposal the author made in 1980 while working on a signage project. The idea was to pave the square in front of the Royal Dutch Library with street stones each carrying one letter and thus displaying some of the texts of the famous books held inside the library. A monospaced font would make it much easier to apply alphabet cobbles. The proposal was never realised, but the idea was revived in the current 'Pyramid' font design for a monospace letter contest in 2012.

Single line stencil fonts

The best fonts to use for cnc routers are so called single line stencil fonts. This type of fonts matches perfectly with the rather straightforward technology of cnc routing. The fonts allow for cutting completely through the base material as well as engraving in it. The selection of the shape of the tool bit and its cutting depth will make it possible to produce endless style variations using the same font. No cnc software is needed to make interpretations of font outlines. The information in the font does not need interpretation, the result of the work is completely under your own control. Considering all these advantages, one would expect a lot of single line stencil fonts to be available. Wrong. Hardly any exist. That is why the author of this book designed a few single line stencil fonts himself, to illustrate his view and hoping that it would generate some interest in this practically completely neglected segment of type design.

Regrettably, the environment to create new single line fonts is lacking. The font world has changed entirely towards servicing outline fonts only. The most used professional font authoring tools do not allow for the production of single line fonts. Most computers will make outlines automatically from text made with an outline font. So one has to turn to the obscurity of proprietary software to realise and use single line fonts. It would be great if software producers would end this unfortunate situation and allow font production specifically for 3d to take off.

Single line stencil fonts are rare. The pictures above show a version that was used for lettering on technical drawings before the arrival of the computer. The version on the left page is one of the very few still in use. It is a typical product of the single line fonts produced for engraving machines. The font allows for many form variations. Underneath, a picture that shows what happens when a single line font is used on your computer.

The following pages show extensive single line stencil fonts designed by the author in an attempt to encourage type designers to get interested in exploring this terra incognita.

Thereafter, a nice collection of stencil fonts is showcased that are suitable for cnc production.

branch of meteorology

the ...ology or cloudology.

Clouds are studied...

nebula.

collect in... interstellar clouds

masses of material

attracted by gravity

A cloud is also a visible

or another planet or...

above the surface...

Manama Cnc™

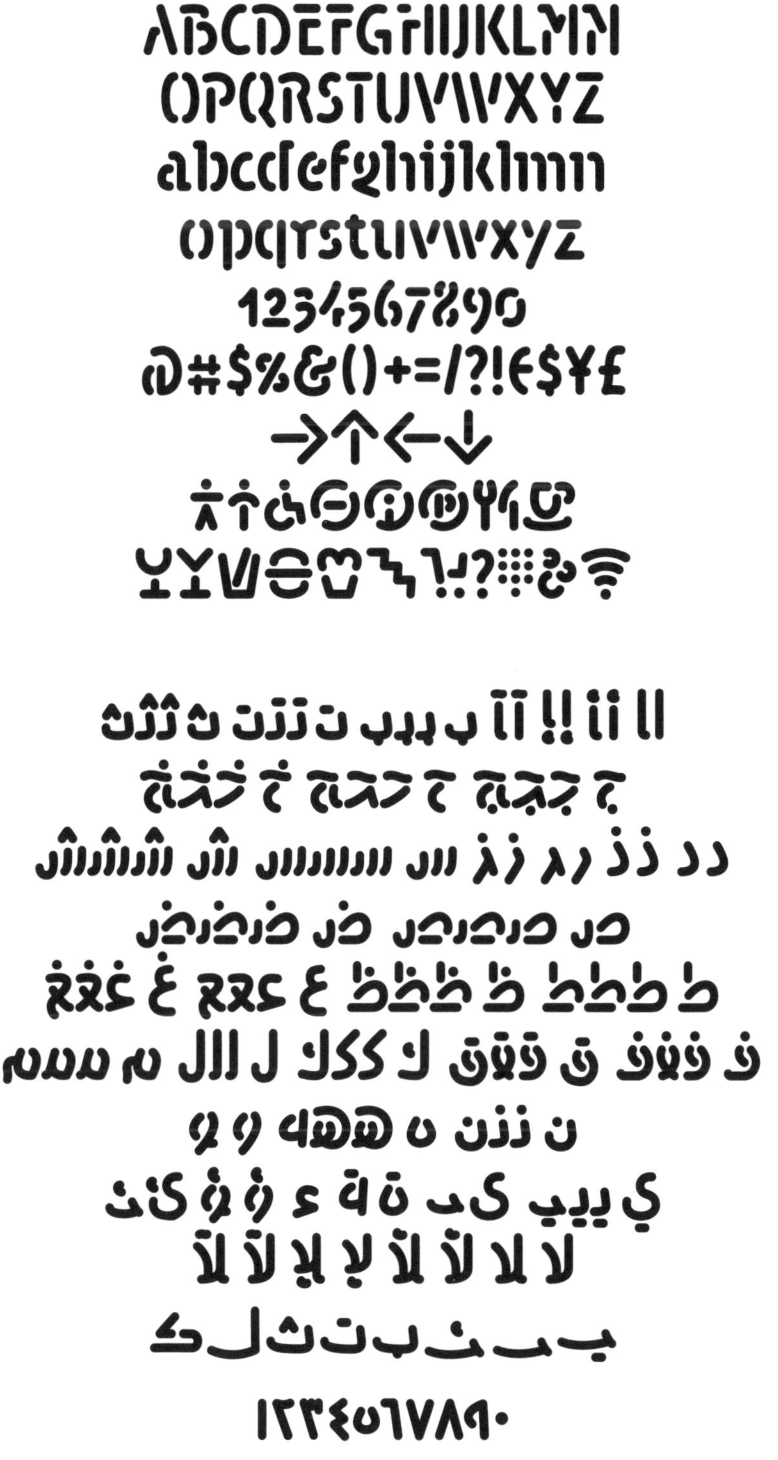

ABCDEFGHIJKLMN
OPQRSTUVWXYZ
abcdefghijklmn
opqrstuvwxyz
1234567890
@#$%&()+=/?!€$¥£
→↑←↓

 كمبيوتر الكتابة العربية

١٢٣٤٥٦٧٨٩٠

Manama Cnc Roman

ABCDEFGHIJKLMN
OPQRSTUVWXYZ
abcdefghijklmn
opqrstuvwxyz
1234567890
@#$%&()+=/?!€$¥£

Manama Cnc Italic

ABCDEFGHIJKLMN
OPQRSTUVWXYZ
abcdefghijklmn
opqrstuvwxyz
1234567890
@$%&()+=/?!€$¥£

Manama Cnc Mix

ABCDEFGHIJKLMN
OPQRSTUVWXYZ
abcdefghijklmn
opqrstuvwxyz
1234567890

Manama Cnc Titling & Swashes

Cnc Stencil Black

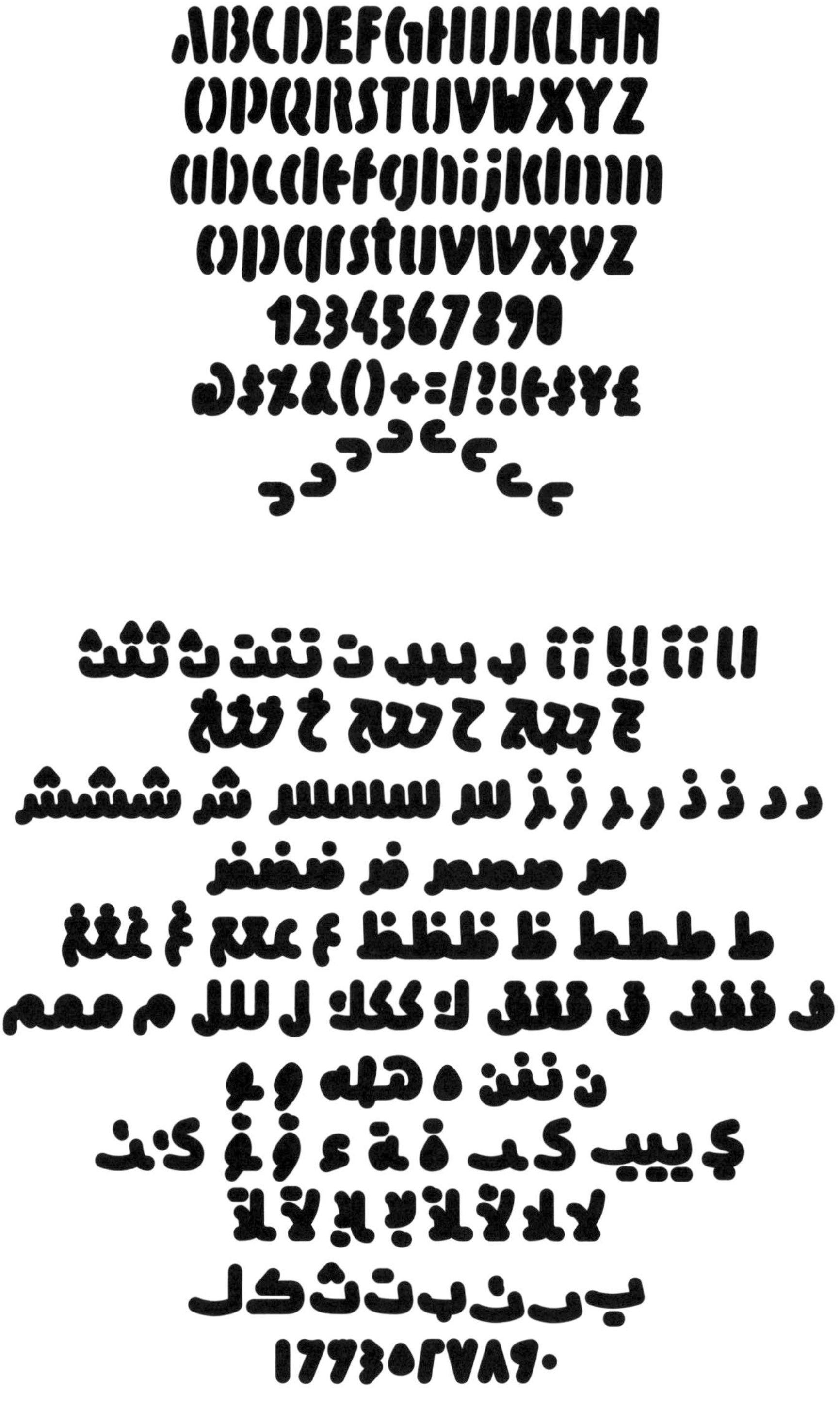

ABCDEFGHIJKLMN
OPQRSTUVWXYZ
abcdefghijklmn
opqrstuvwxyz
1234567890
@$%&()+=/?!￡$¥€

ا ا ا ئٹ إ!أ ئ أٹ ب ببب ت تتت ت ثث
ج ججج ح ححح خ ججخ
د د ذ ذ ر رز سر سسسر شر ششش
ص صصص ض ضضض
ط ططط ظ ظظظظ ع ععع غ غغغ
ف ففف ق ققق لا ككك ل للل م ممم
ن ننن ه ههه و ؤ
ي ييي كد ة ة ء ؤ ؤ كن
لآ لأ لأ لإ لإ لا لا
ب ب ث ت ث كل
١٢٣٤٥٦٧٨٩٠

'Titling'
&
'Swashes'
'Alternates'

'Titling'
&
'Swashes'
'Alternates'

FP Palina (Fontpartners)

ABCDEFGHIJKLMN
OPQRSTUVWXYZ
1234567890
/?!

Giambo Stencil (Rodrigo Fuenzalida)

ABCDEFGHIJKLMN
OPQRSTUVWXYZ
abcdefghiklmn
opqrstuvwxyz
1234567890
@#%&()+=/?!€$¥£

Signed JNL (Jeff Levine)

ABCDEFGHIJKLMN
OPQRSTUVWXYZ
abcdefghijklmn
opqrstuvwxyz
1234567890
@#%&()+=/?!€$¥£

Couteau Stencil (Pierre Pane-Farre)

ABCDEFGHIJKLMN
OPQRSTUVWXYZ
abcdefghijklmn
opqrstuvwxyz
1234567890
@%&()+=/?!€$¥£

Puncho Stencil (Fred Smeijers)

ABCDEFGHIJKLMN
OPQRSTUVWXYZ
abcdefghijklmn
opqrstuvwxyz
1234567890
¡¿&()+=/?!€$¥£

Orly Stencil (Pierre Pane-Farre)

ABCDEFGHIJKLMN
OPQRSTUVWXYZ
abcdefghijklmn
opqrstuvwxyz
1234567890
@&()+=/?!€$¥£

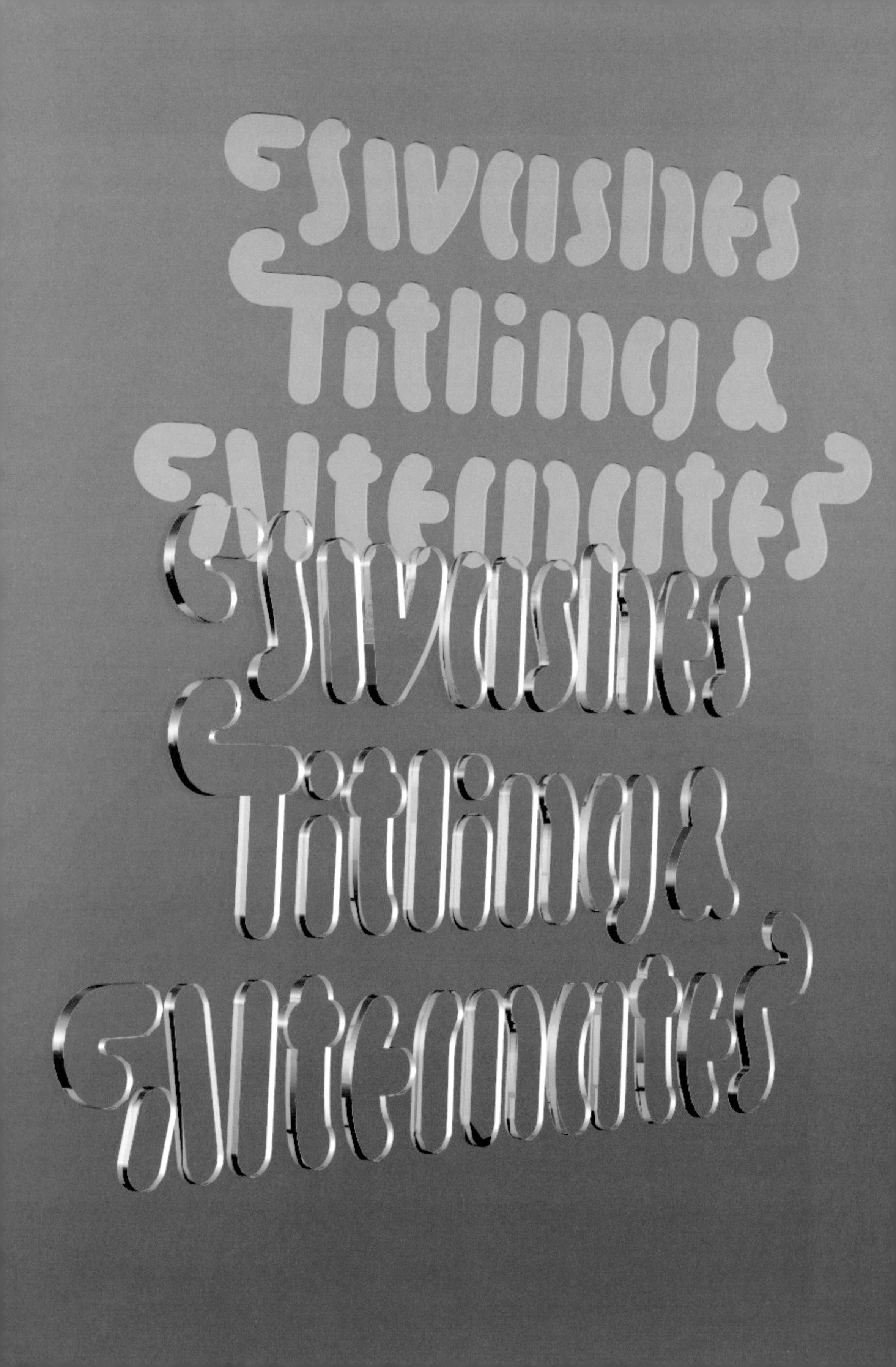

Sivashes
Titling &
alternates
Sivashes
Titling &
alternates

The Golden Hen

Toilets →
↑ Restaurant
← Parking

Restaurant ↑

Toilets →

Toilets →

Parking ↓

ets →

8 Showcase

The last part of this book is entirely dedicated to showcasing examples of using 3d lettering in the private or public space. Both are territories anxiously awaiting further and deeper professional exploration. We are much used to see text in our environment, in some cases, there may even be a bit too much of it. But all of these texts have an advertising or informational purpose, while text can serve so many more other goals. The visual art world invented 'concrete poetry' during the 1950s. Typography usually serves the content of a text, helping to make it as easily accessible as possible. With concrete poetry, the visual shape becomes an inseparable part of its meaning. It requires a different professional approach to typography.

This aspect is also important when exploring options for sculpting type to become a long-time part of our environment. Designers have to step away from the conventional manner we judge text and typography. Usually, we will weigh their qualities of legibility and comprehensibility. But these values are only important when the purpose of the text is to guide or inform us. After this purpose is served, we no longer need the text and even may wish it to disappear. As we put away a newspaper or a magazine after reading them. But we do not only appreciate text for its purely functional purpose. The text in our environment also creates a sense of accessibility. Imagine a city without any text at all. It would be quite a desolate place. Our minds like to be informed, but they also like to be given the impression of availability, of attractiveness, fun and mystery.

Poets (priests and politicians) play with the ambiguity in the meaning of words. Words and symbols with an obscure meaning can have a huge impact on people's minds. It will certainly attract their natural curiosity more than plain language. Even seven year old boys already know all about that. Comprehensibility will certainly help us, but it is unlikely to excite us. We feel an irresistible attraction to the mysteries of hocus-pocus.

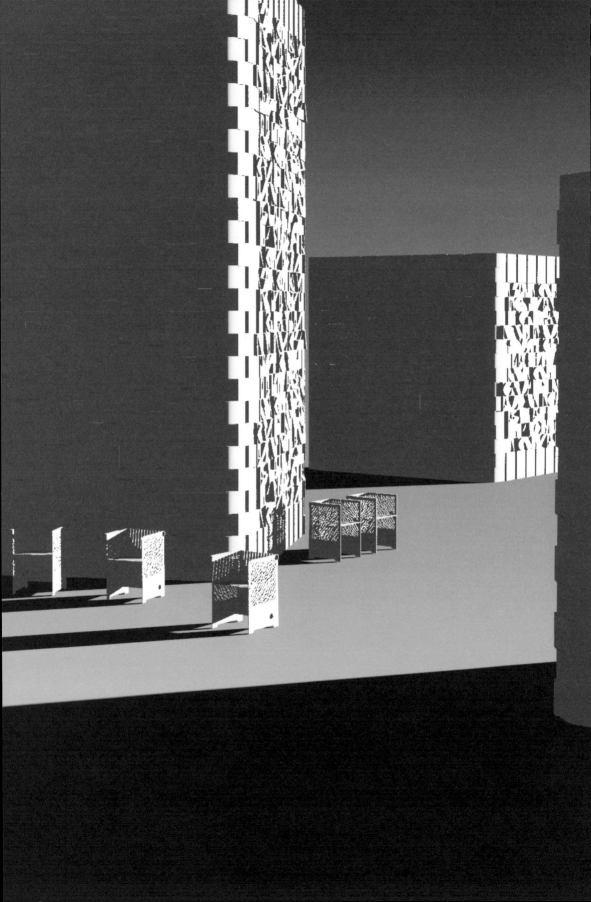

We may assign magical power to formulas or symbols we do not understand. That's how our mind works. And we must use this aspect when sculpting type for the environment. This type of typography must have the quality of keeping us intrigued, so it had better be a bit mysterious and not too plain. Legibility is certainly not a priority. This is not text to help us make the right decisions at the right moments, such as we demand of the text on traffic signs. This type of text does not have to reveal its meaning instantly. Better not. It's lasting attractiveness is better served with some level of obscurity. All art keeps us fantasising about its true meaning. Artists know that and try to add to the mystery in their explanations of their own work. The Mona Lisa must keep her mysterious smile. A piece of art must allow us to attach our own fantasies to it. There is room for a more poetic approach to applying 3d text in the private and the public sphere. This approach will make use of the spiritual, metaphorical, or even the metaphysical, enigmatic and occult powers that text and symbols can have.

The samples show mostly the experiments of the author. His studies cover a wide range, from studies to create 3d alphabets to straightforward applications in furniture designs. A large part of the showcase, however, is taken by the more dreamy applications. And not hindered by considerations of feasibility. It is best to start design work by dreaming away. Feasibility constraints will set in automatically at some stage or other. Fantasy is our only option to warp reality.

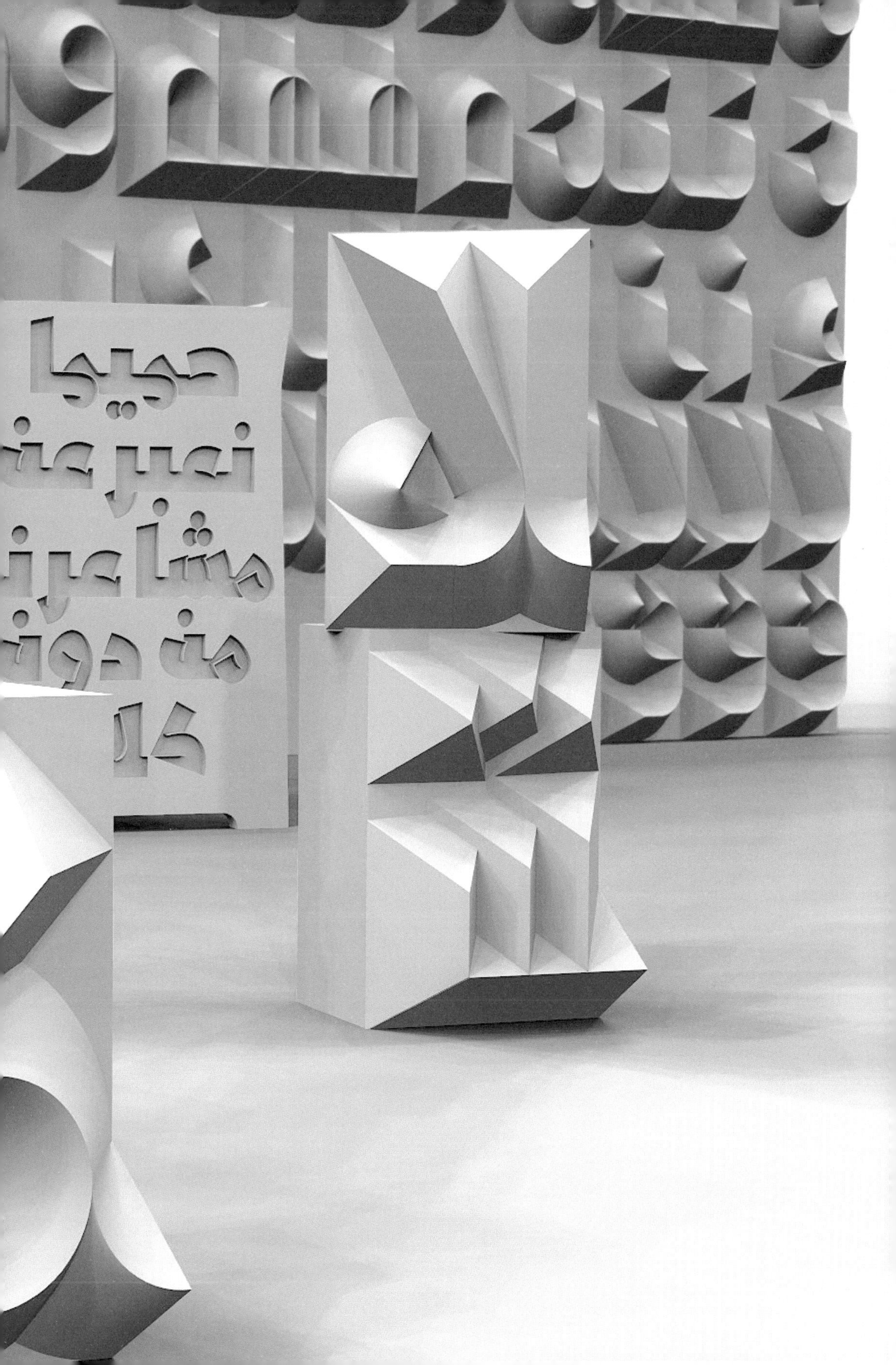

نعبر عن

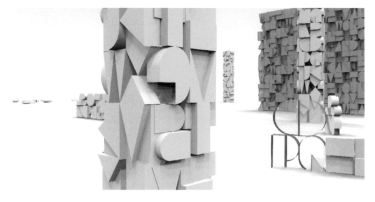

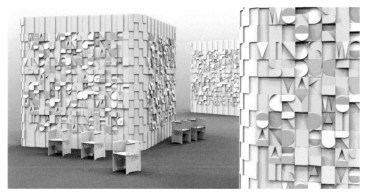

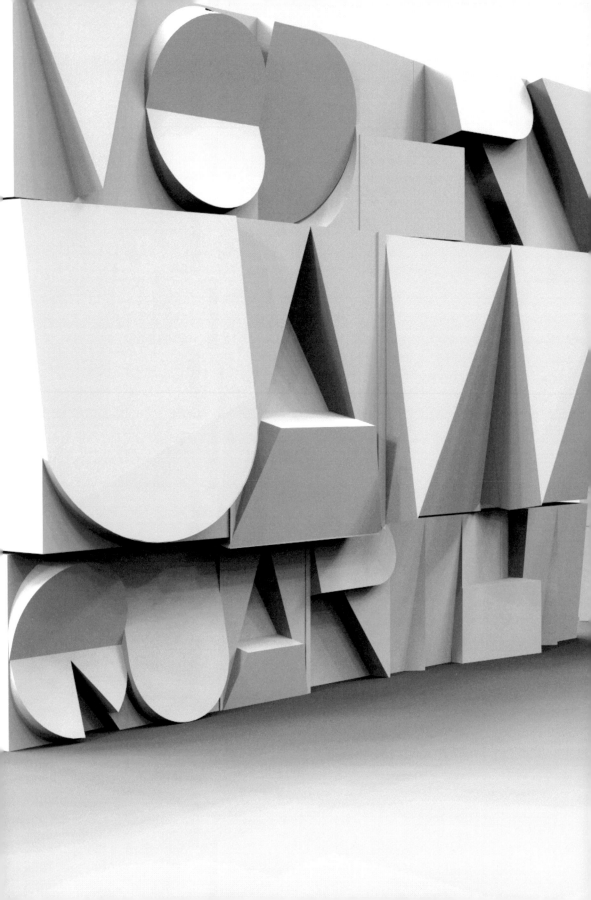

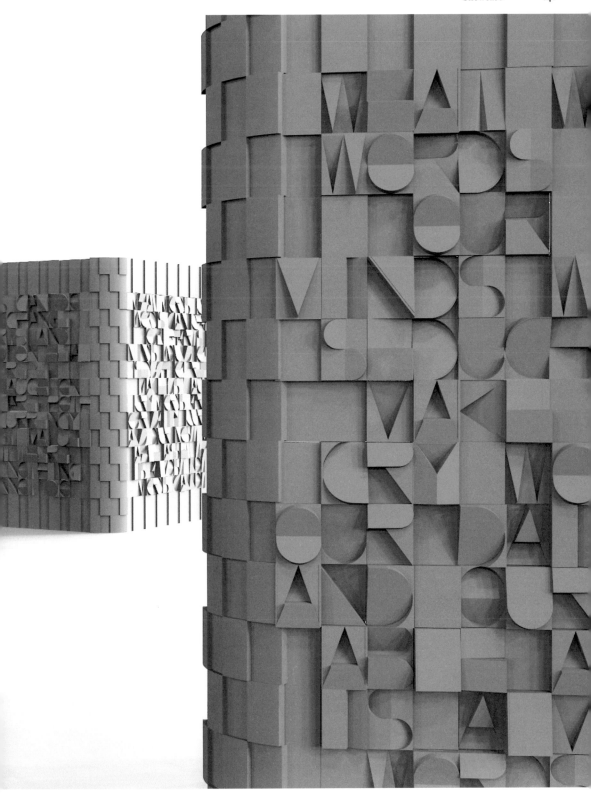

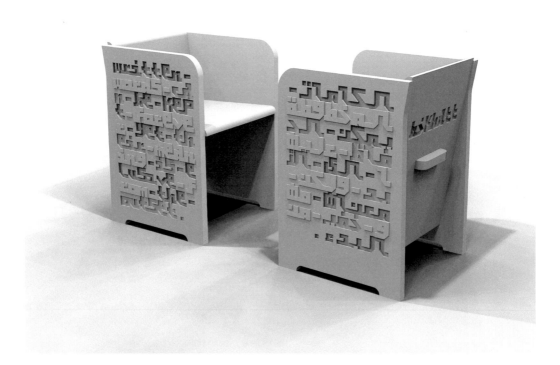

لقد وصلت في نهاية
هذا التاريخ العظيم
وجميع الأراضي وسوف
تتحدث عن لي: أنا لا
تموت وهذه البذور لقد
زرعت سيوفي اسمي
وسمعته من القيم
والرجال من معنى
والحكمة وسوف تعلن
وعندما ذهبت يشيد
بلادي والشهرة لي.

 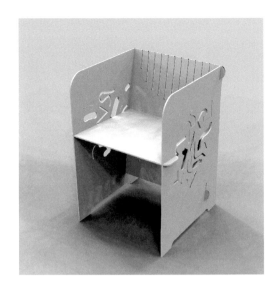

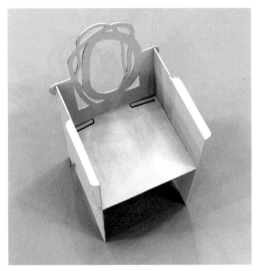 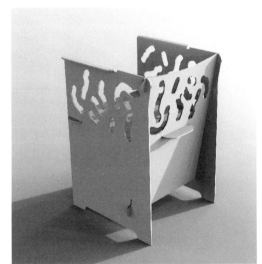

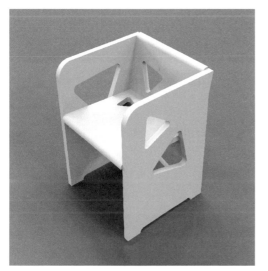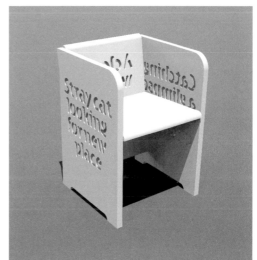
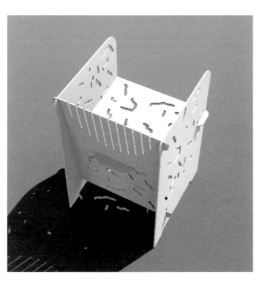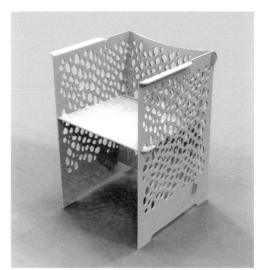
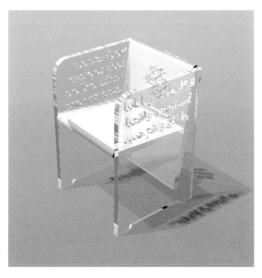

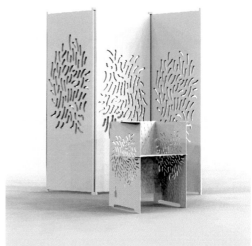

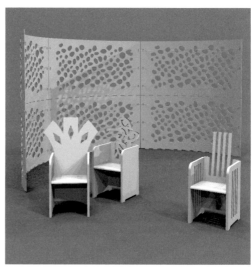

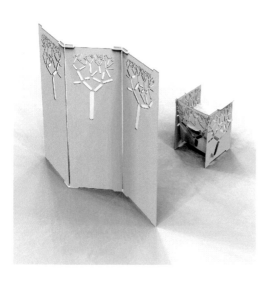

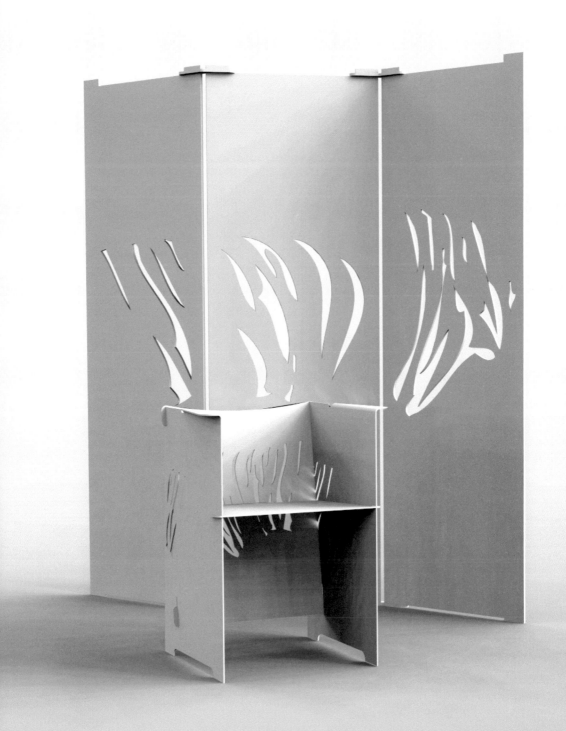

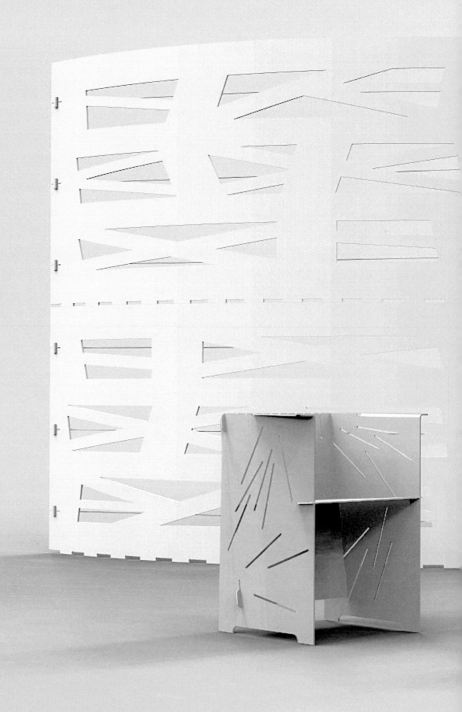

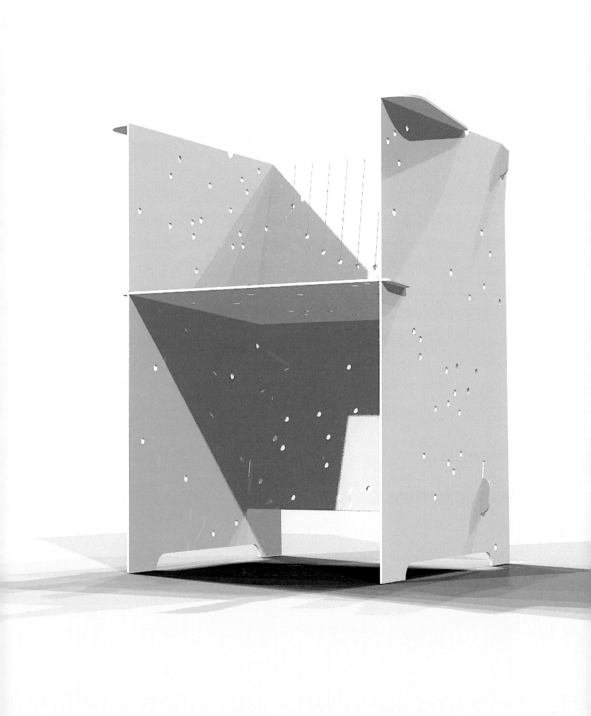

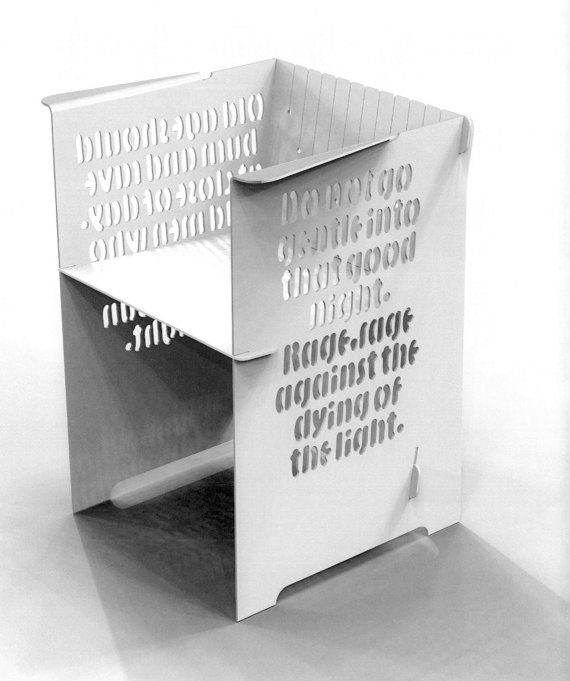

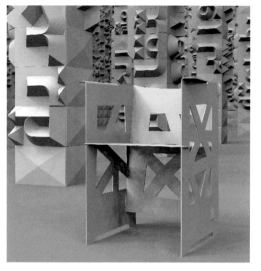

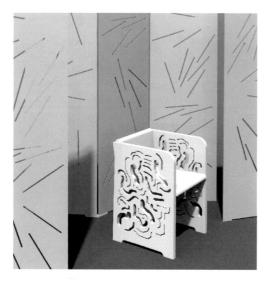

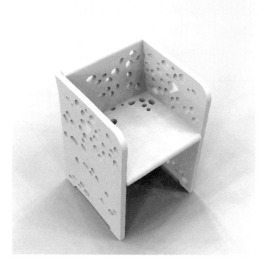
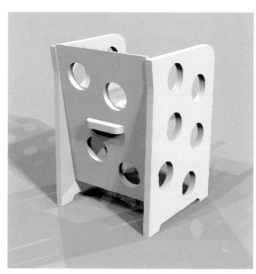
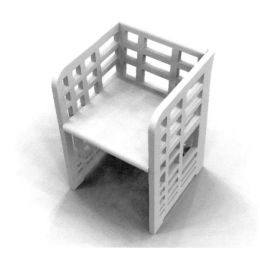
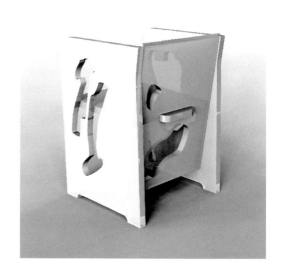

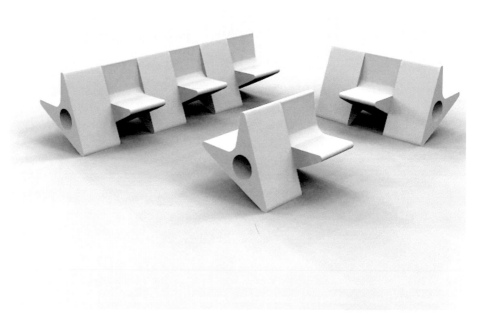

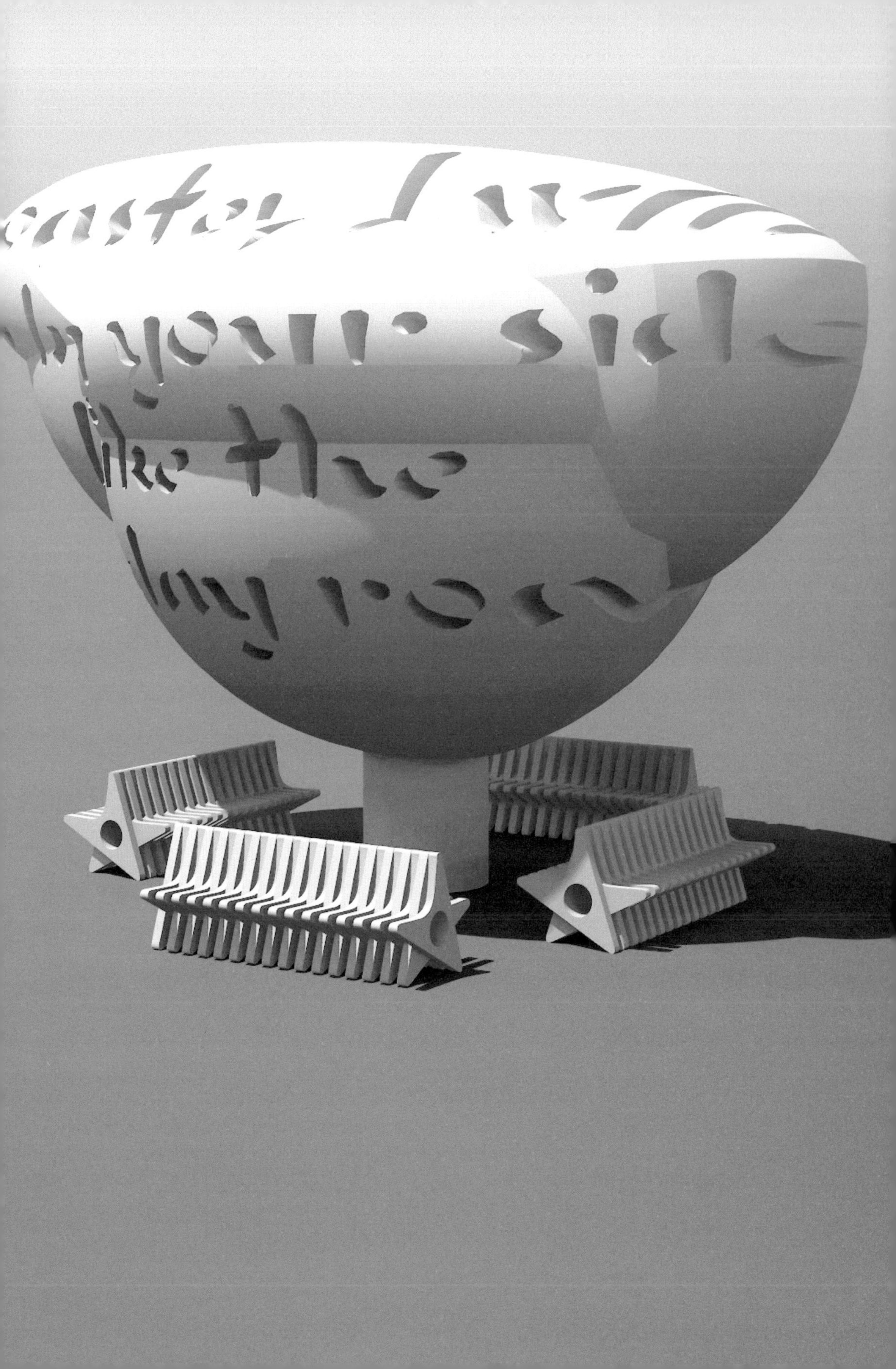
your
like the

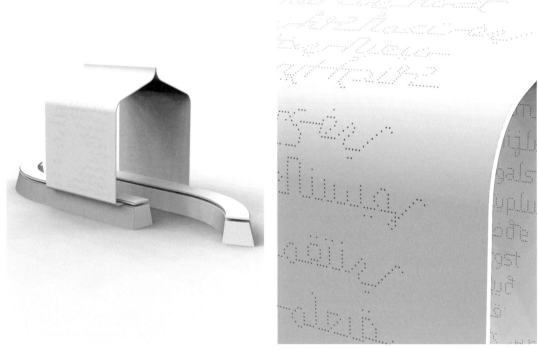

Designs by Jeroen van Erp

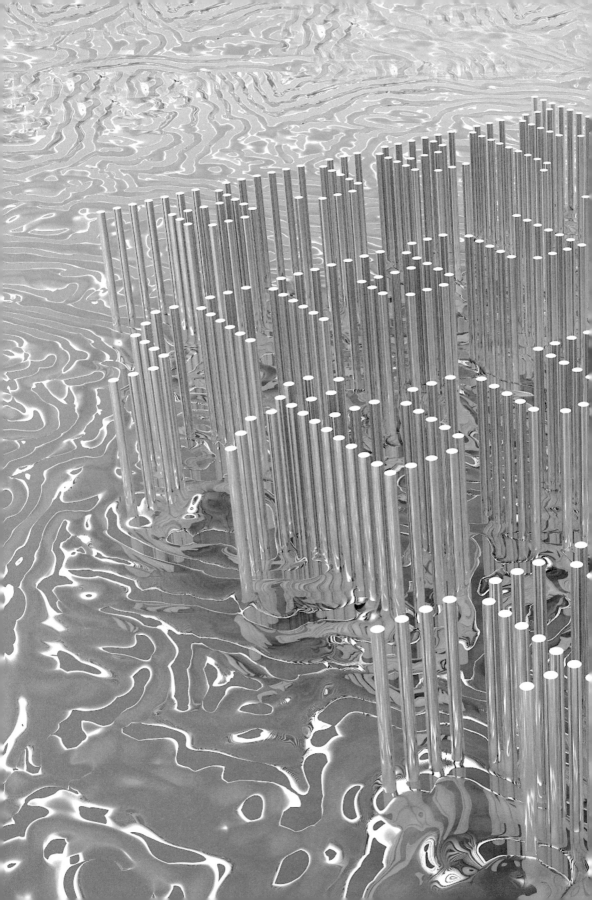

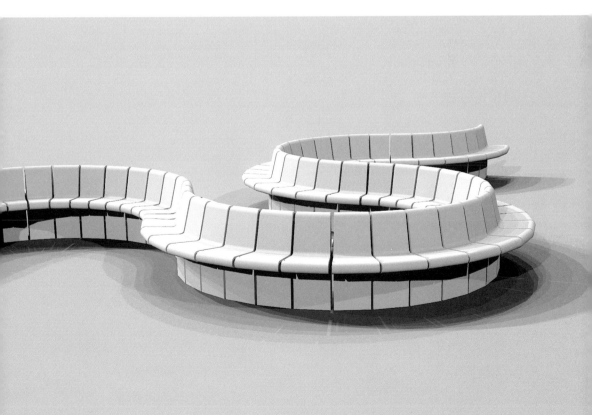

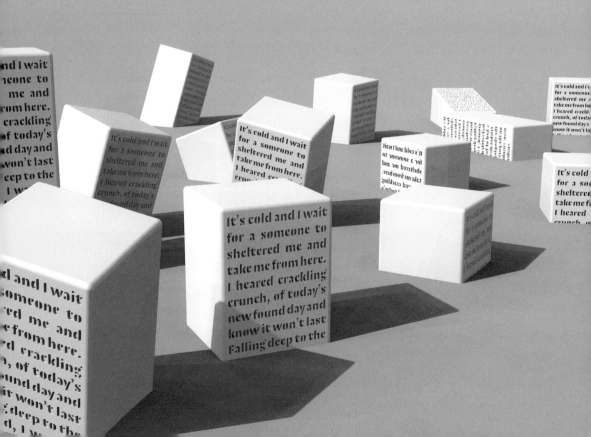

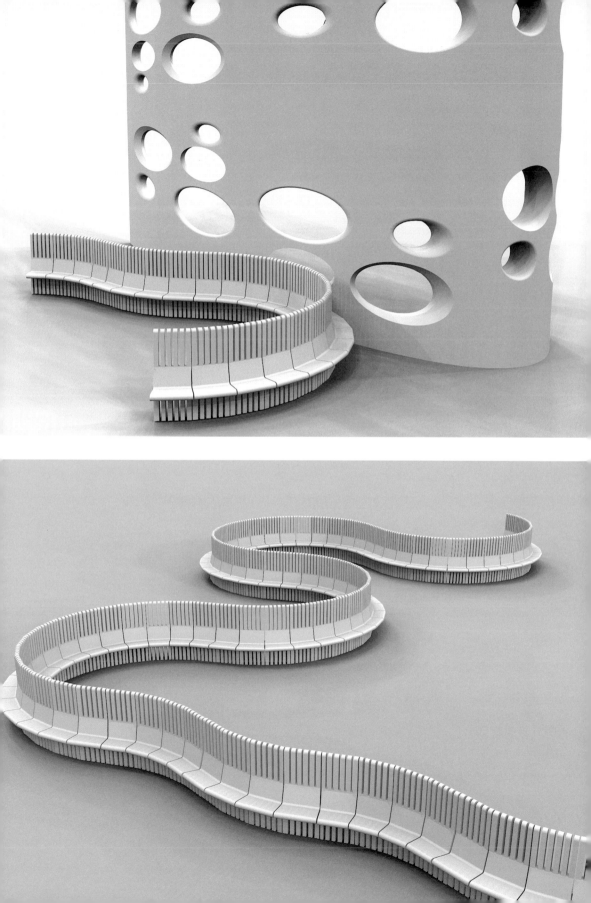

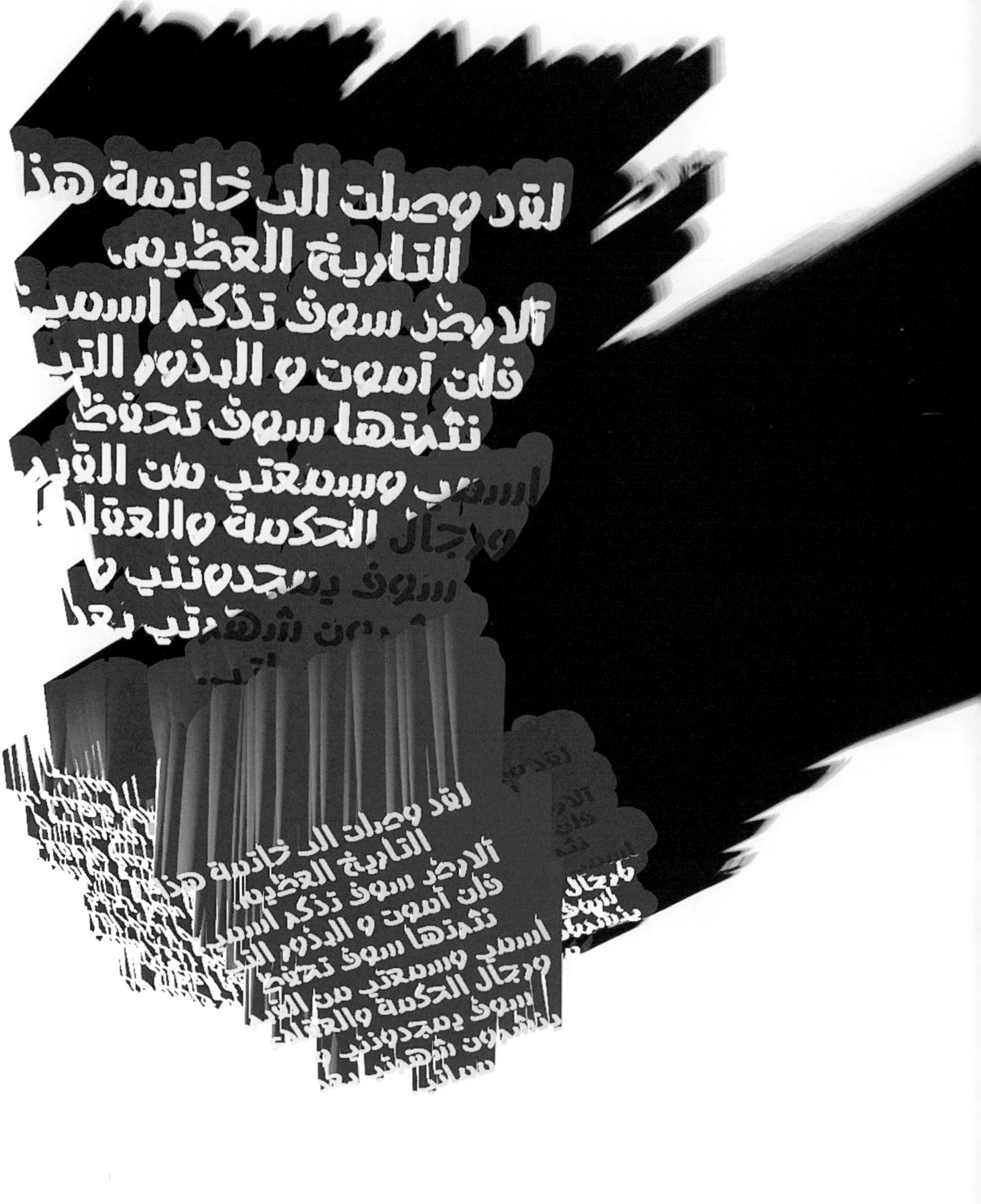

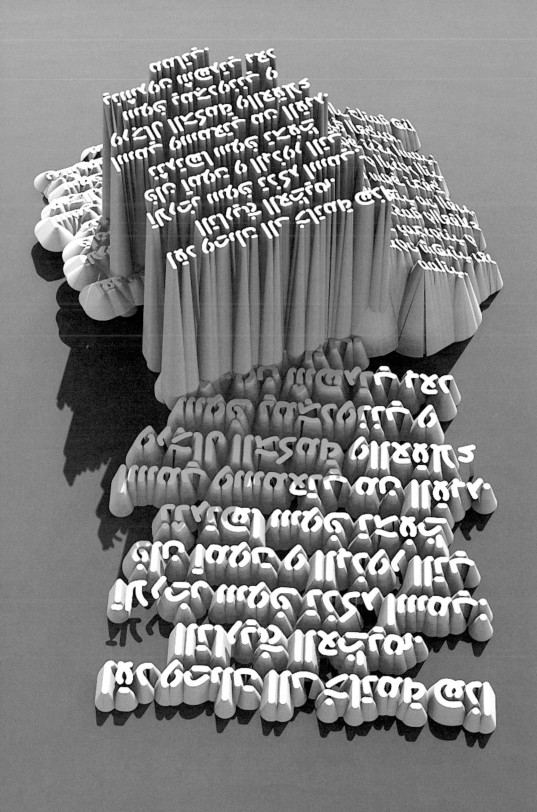

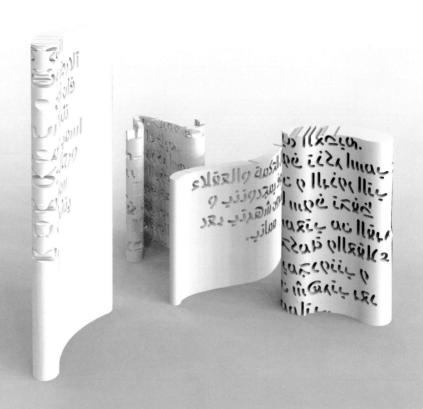
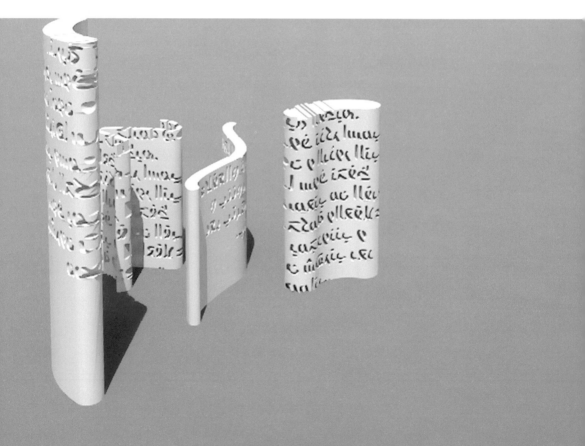

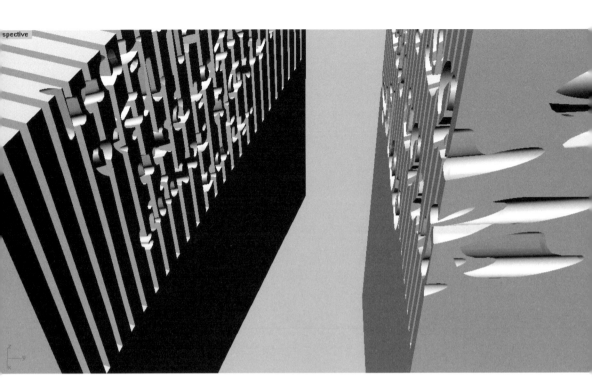

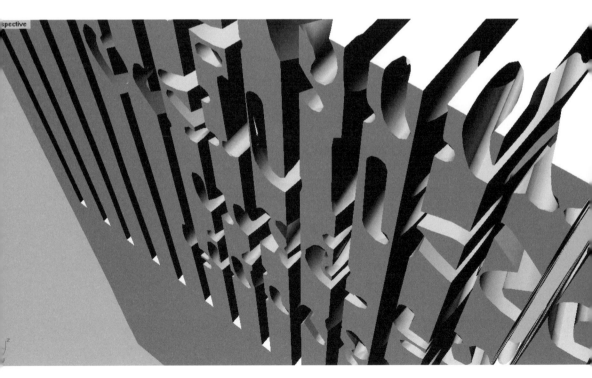

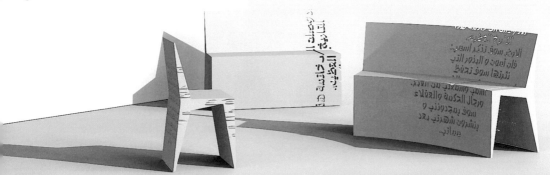

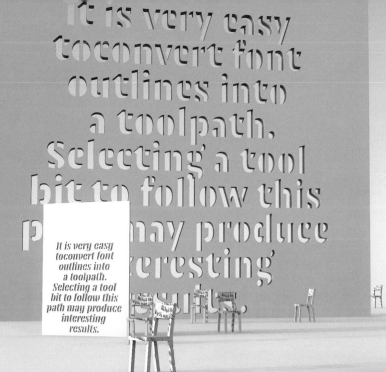

It is very easy
toconvert font
outlines into
a toolpath.
Selecting a tool
bit to follow this
path may produce
interesting
results.

It is very easy
toconvert font
outlines into
a toolpath.
Selecting a tool
bit to follow this
path may produce
interesting
results.

It is very easy toconvert font outlines into a toolpath. Selecting a tool bit to follow this path may produce interesting results.

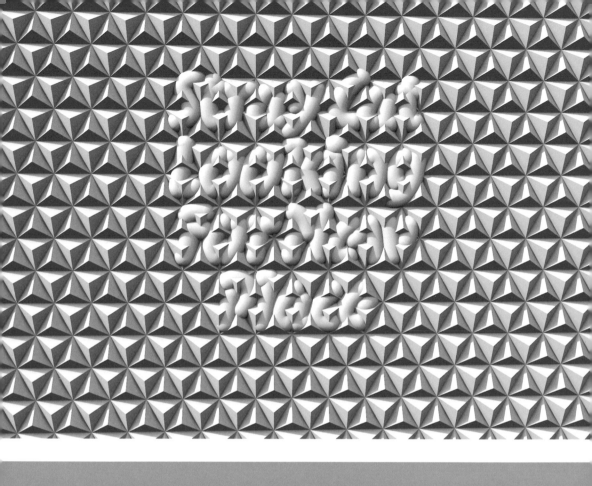

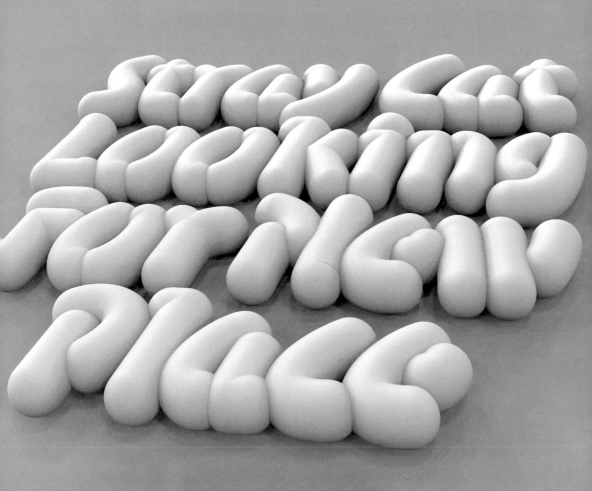

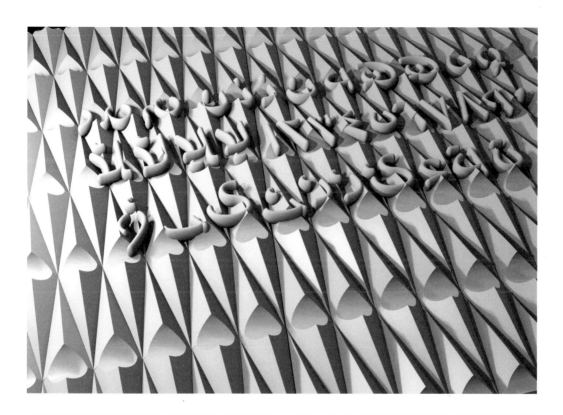

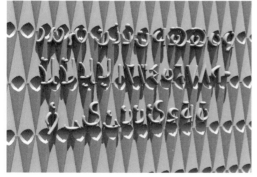

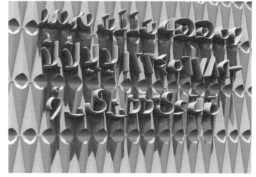

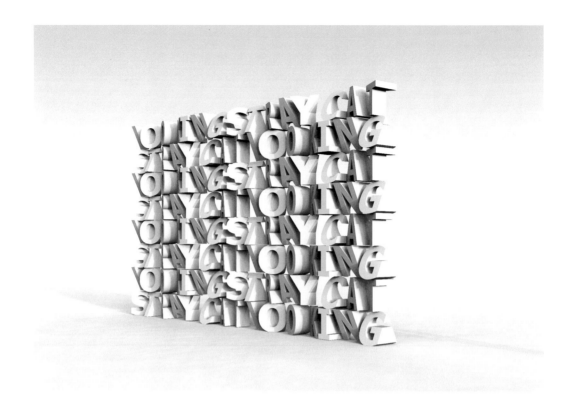

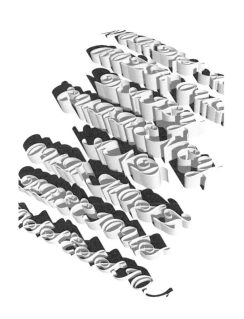

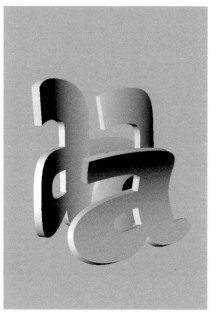

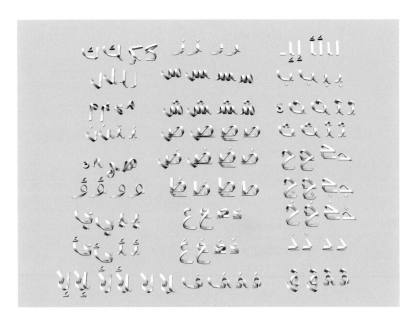

The Kasheeda typeface, Arabic part designed by Yara Khoury. On the overleaf pages shown in combination with the Storyline typeface, designed by Max Kisman and Naji El Mir.

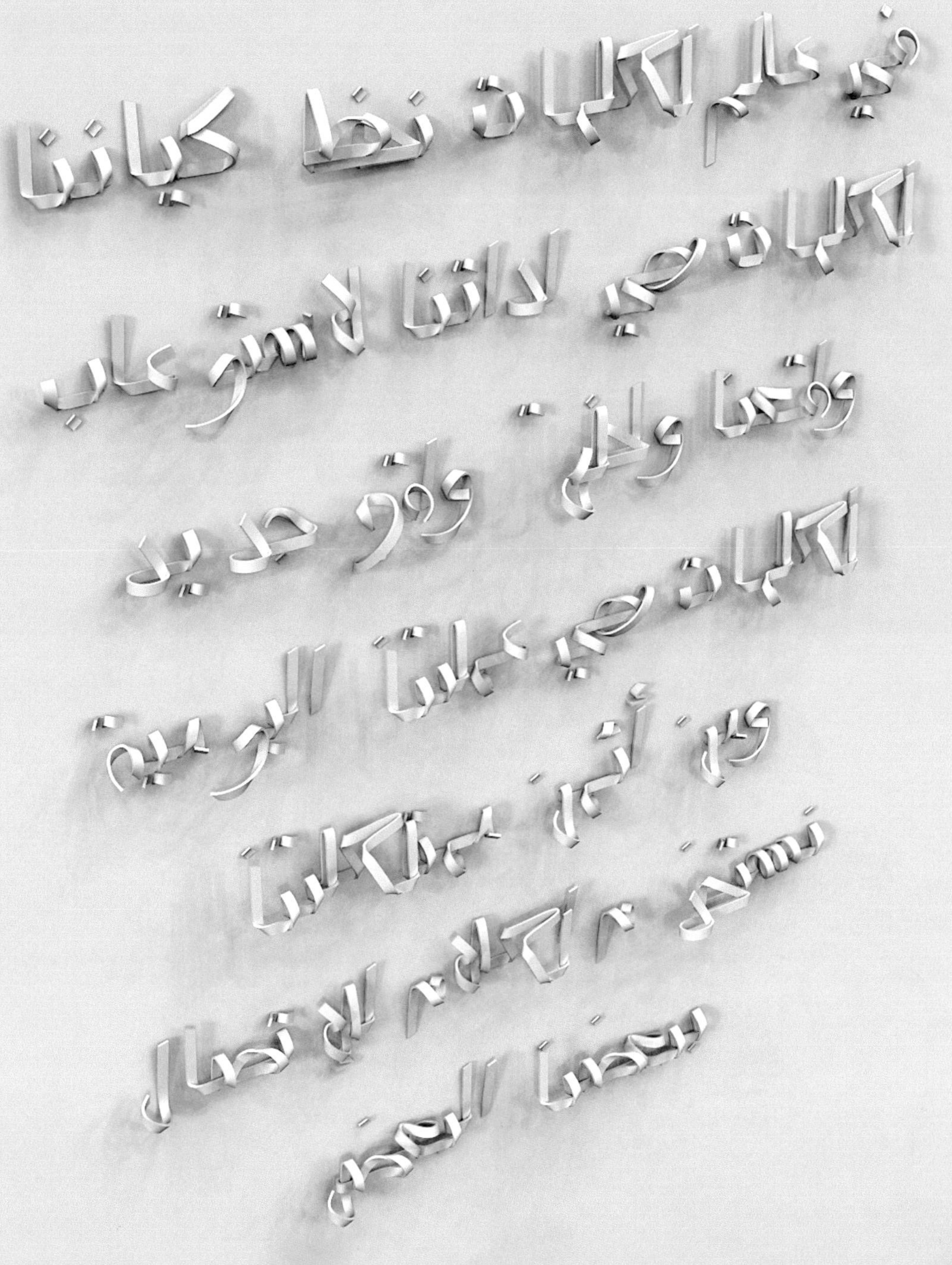
في عالم الكلمات نخلق كياننا
الكلمات هي أداتنا لاستيعاب
واقعنا وخلق وجود جديد
الكلمات هي علاقتنا الروحية
مع أنفسنا بكلماتنا
نستخدم الكلام للاتصال
ببعضنا البعض

The Kasheeda typeface, Latin part designed
by Melle Hammer.

words are the tool revise reality and create a new

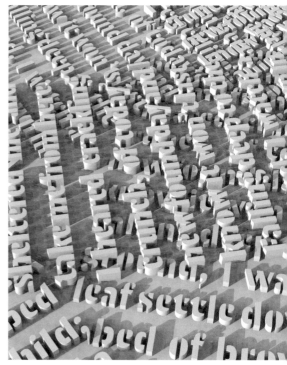

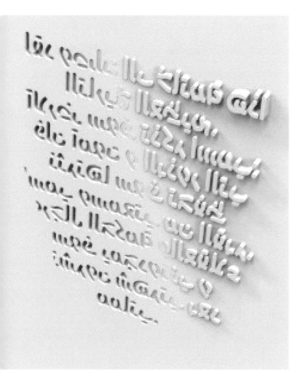

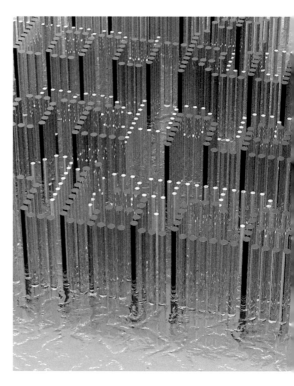

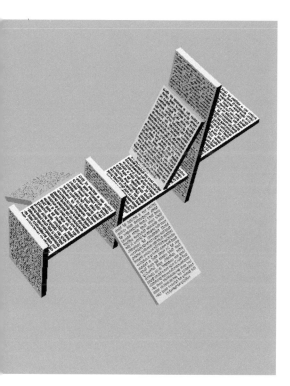

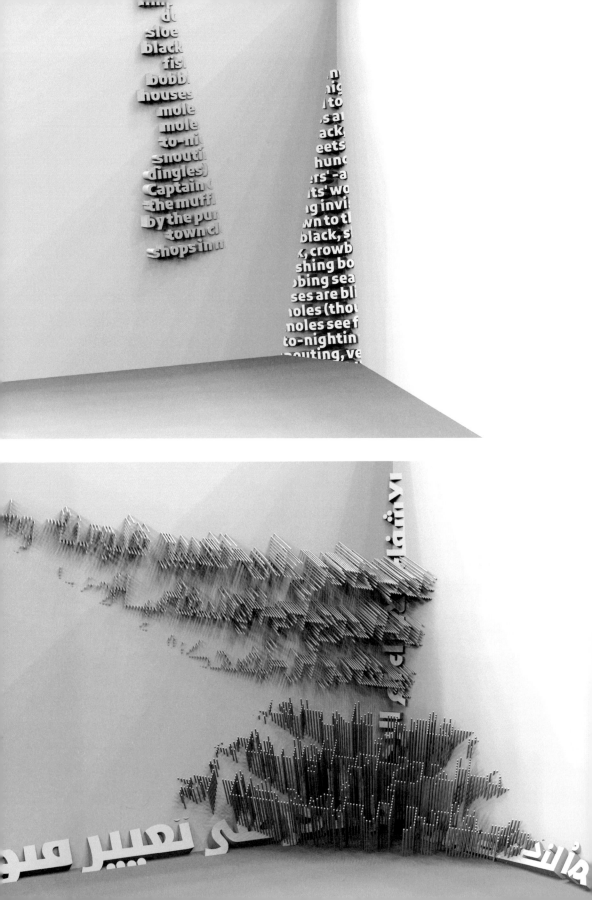

قادر على تغيير من

در على تغيير قلوبنا وارائنا.
... أم الشفاء، الإغراء أم الردي،
... أم يبكينا

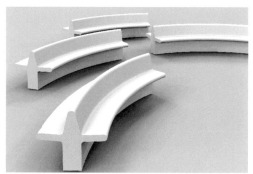

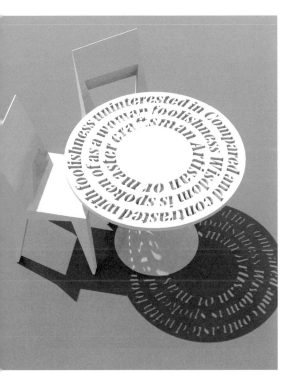

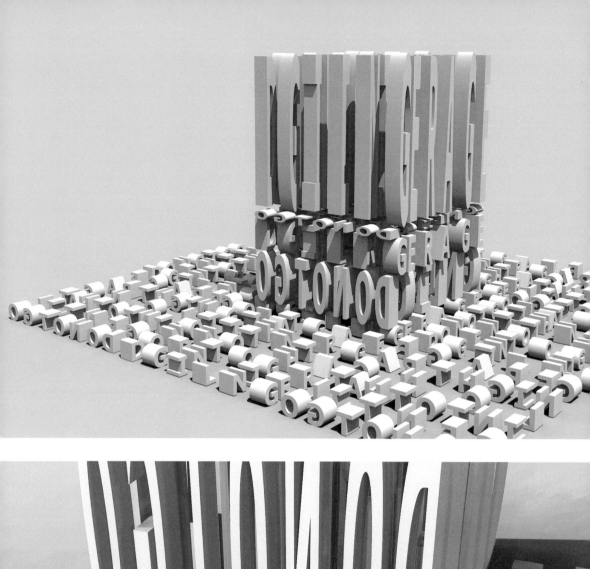

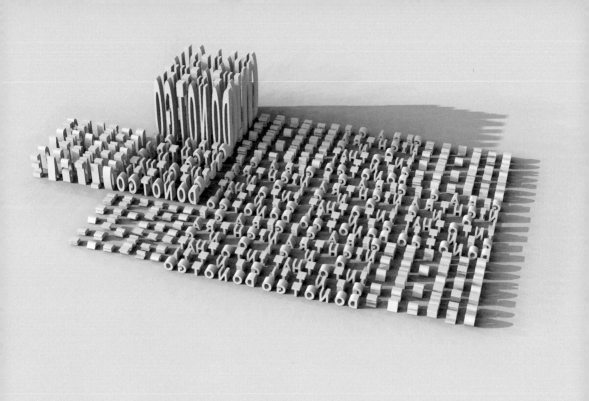

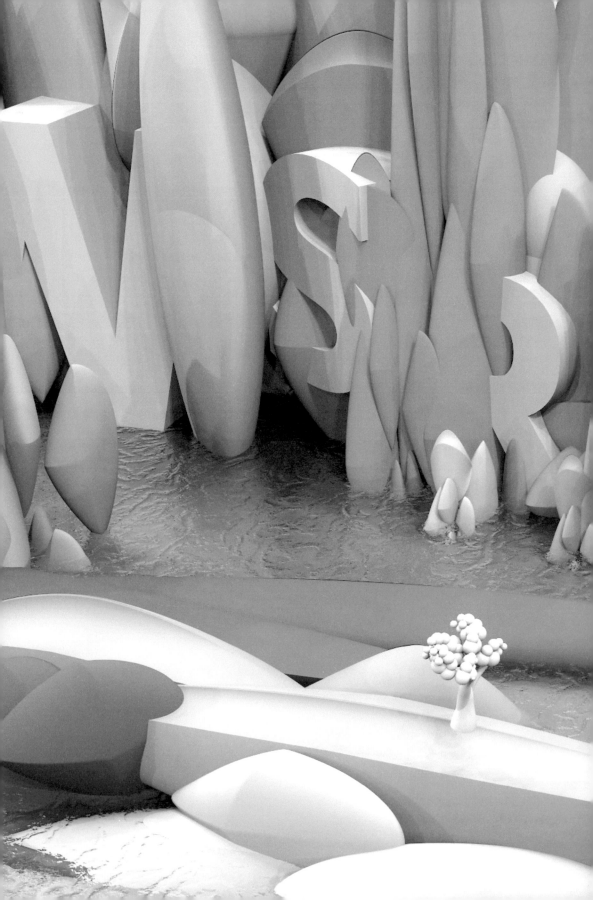

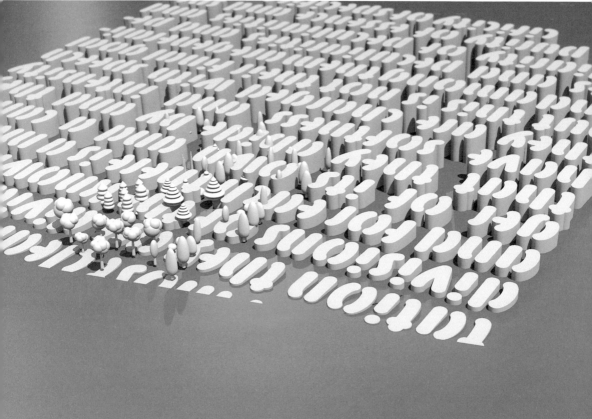

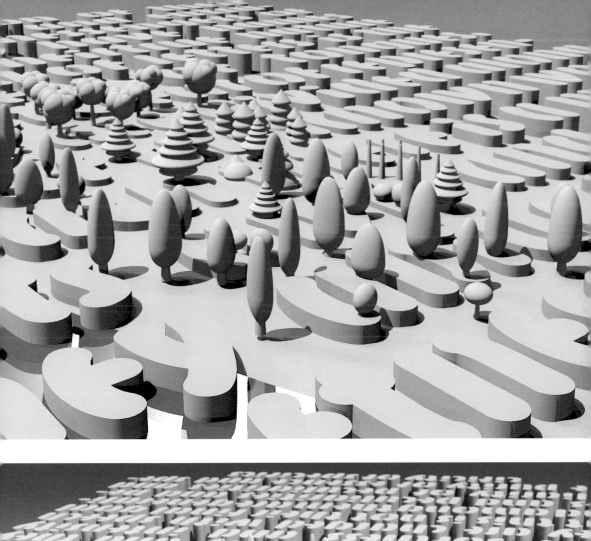

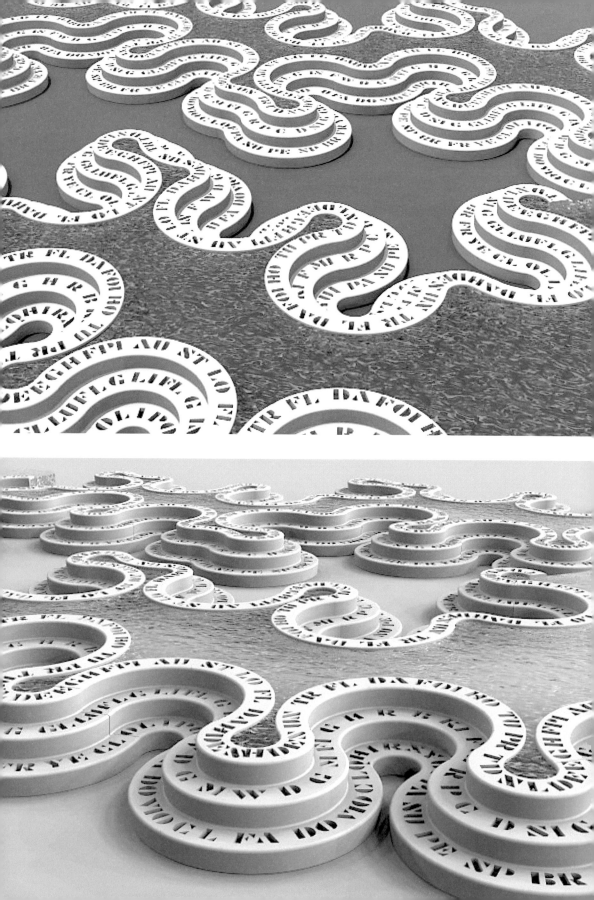

9 Acknowledgements

The idea to write this book started with my interest in the designs produced for the Typographic Matchmaking in the City project, curated by Huda AbiFares. This project tried to explore the use of typography in the built environment by assigning five Dutch/Arab mixed teams of type, graphic, product designers and architects to develop five typefaces and propose possible applications for them in public space. This project, initiated by the Khatt Foundation and funded by the Dutch Ministry of Culture (Mondriaan Fund) was totally unique, and on this scale nothing even remotely comparable was ever attempted before.

During this inspiring kickstart introduction in this new field I began to explore production alternatives only to discover that manufacturing options were endless but hardly explored for typography. There are no books on this field other than a few I consulted about letter carving. For the rest, I studied documentation released by a number of tool manufacturers and that is made publicly available on their websites and elsewhere discussed on the web.

I thank all participants of the Typographic Matchmaking in the City project, and Huda AbiFares in particular for giving me the initial inspiration. I show a few of their products in my book. I went as far as designing a new typeface specifically for easy cnc reproduction. I called this 'single line' font the 'Manama cnc' after the city where the font was first applied. The Lebanese type designer Khajag Apelian has been indispensable in the creation of this font. A very special thanks also to product designer Maurits de Koning who I asked to help me to realise prototypes of designs by producing the initial 3d digital files. He made the incredibly wise, kind and unselfish decision to make himself redundant in the production process by advising me to learn to use a specific 3d modelling software (Rhinoceros) myself. Without his advice this book would have looked totally different. Rutger Graas is another designer/cabinetmaker who was very important for me to understand production options. I'm very grateful for his advice, dedication and patience to actually produce my prototypes. There was another piece of software I had to learn. It is called 'Aspire' and is developed by the British 'Vectric Ltd' company. I used this software to test and visualise a large number of my designs and used these renderings as illustrations in my book. Vectric lets designers use a trial version of their software. (The machine instructions are disabled in this version, so you cannot produce your designs). I'm grateful for their generous offer to use their fine and useful software for free.

There is one source of information that has become almost indispensable for all of us. This source is called 'Googling the Web'. I have used it a lot and it has helped me tremendously to find information and to find illustrations and even inspiring artwork. The abundance of the web makes one careless, you should make detailed notes of your sources. That is really tough when using the web. At least for me. So I apologise when I do not mention a source I should have mentioned, because I simply forgot it.

Finally, I have to thank Huda AbiFares for proofreading the text first, Michael Forder for doing the same as a professional and Pantheon Drukkers for producing a wonderfully printed book.

Edo Smitshuijzen, March 2013

Illustration List

Most illustrations were produced by the author. Illustrations downloaded from various sources on the internet can be found on the following pages: 9, 33, 35, 36, 37, 39, 40, 54, 55, 58, 65, 73, 74, 78, 79, 80, 81, 82, 83, 88, 90, 91, 92, 93, 102, 103, 110, 113. Some of the natural patterns applied as decorations for the designs were also downloaded from the web. The author used the typefaces that were developed for the 'Typographic Matchmaking in the City' project to make some new applications of his own design. The captions will inform about the source of the illustration when known or still remembered by the author.
Every effort has been made to credit the sources of the illustrations. Please inform the publisher in case rectifications are required for a following edition.

محدد. صمم مؤلف الكتاب هذا عدداً من الخطوط الثلاثية الأبعاد لسبب بسيط، هو أنه لم يكن هناك تصاميم خطية متوافرة لاستعراض الاستعمالات الممكنة. لا تزال هناك مجالات شاسعة ضمن التصميم الخطّي الاحترافي لما يتطرق إليها أحدٌ بعد؛ وكون مئات التصاميم الخطّية تُنتَّج يومياً لا يعني شيءً بحد ذاته، ذلك أن معظمها لا يتعدى كونه تمريناً في الأسلوب.

هذا الكتاب هو محاولة لتعزيز الاهتمام بالتيبوغرافيا ثلاثية الأبعاد؛ في النهاية، هناك طرقٌ عديدة لاستعمال المعلومات الرقمية نفسها التي تُستخدم في الإنتاج الثنائي الأبعاد، وتوظيفها في نظيره الثلاثي الأبعاد. إن إنتاج أشياء ملموسة هو أمرٌ سهل حقاً، ولقد أصبح توظيف كل أنواع المعلومات الرقمية، التي نستخدمها يومياً، في مجال الإنتاج ثلاثي الأبعاد أمراً فائق البساطة. هناك مجموعة هائلة من الأنواع المختلفة من قاطعات السي أن سي (القابلة للتحكم الرقمي بالكمبيوتر)، وهي قادرة على تطبيق جميع أنواع الملفات الرقمية تقريباً على مواد برقة الورق (وبصغر النملة)، كما أنها قادرة على تطبيقها على مواد كبيرة، أكان ذلك زجاجاً بسماكة عدة سنتيمترات أو حجراً أو معدناً أو أي مواد ممكن تخيلها، وبأحجام خيالية حتى علو المباني مثلاً. فضلاً عن هذا، فقد تم تطوير برامج خاصة قادرة على تحويل قاطعات السي أن سي البسيطة إلى آلات قادرة على إنتاج أشياء مذهلة للعين.

«التصنيع الزيادي» (أو الطباعة الثلاثية الأبعاد، أو التمذجة السريعة، أو الليبوغرافيا الصوتية) هي جميعها أسماء متداولة لأحدث فرع في شجرة التكنولوجيا متناهية النمو، وهي جميعها سوف تحوّل التصنيع إلى نشاط مكتبي. لقد قامت هذه التكنولوجيا بإزالة كل العقبات التقليدية للإنتاج الصناعي؛ أي شكل ممكن طالما أنه لا ينهار تحت ثقل ذاته. إن مجال تصنيع الأشياء الملموسة هو سهل الولوج، وهو بانتظار مصممين/ات مهرة في التصميم والتواصل لكي يطلقوا العنان لأحلامهم/ن، ولكي يستكشفوا هذا العالم الجديد بإنتاجاته الأكثر ديمومة من إنتاجات مجالهم الاحترافي التقليدي. إن خلفيتهم الخلاقة هي قادرة على تذليل العقبات التقليدية، وبيئتنا المَعاشة قادرة على أن تغتني بإنتاجات آنية من عالم لا تسبر غوره عادةً إلا الكتب والمجلات والشاشات.

يشكل هذا الكتاب دعوةً للمصممين/ات لكي يحققوا الرؤية هذه، وهو يشرح المبادئ الأساسية في تقنيات التصنيع المختلفة، كما يشرح خيارات الإنتاج ومشاكلها وأفضل الطرق لمعالجتها. على أن الأهم من هذا كله هو أنه يستعرض تصاميم جديدة يحاول المؤلف عبرها أن يرفع الغطاء عن صندوق لامتناهي العمق قد طال إغلاقه.

المقدمة

رغم غرابة الأمر، فإن هذا الكتاب هو الأول الذي يتناول كيفية استحداث تيبوغرافيا ثلاثية الأبعاد عبر استخدام آلات السي أن سي (أي آلات قابلة للتحكم الرقمي بالكمبيوتر computer numerical control). لطالما كانت التيبوغرافيا المحضرة لإستعمالات ثلاثية الأبعاد يتيمة في مجال التصميم، أي أنّها لم تكن تحظى سوى باهتمام الحرفيين. بالفعل، فإنه ثمة بعض المصممين/ات الذين يعتبرون أن تعلم نحت سبائك الحروف المعدنية هو أمر أساسي لإتقان حرفة التصميم، إلا أن معظم المصممين/ات الخطّين/ات (ناهيك عن المصممين الغرافيكيين) يرتاحون أكثر بالبقاء ضمن العالم الثنائي الأبعاد. واقع الحال أن الممارسة اليومية للتصميم الخطّي تعنى بتفاصيل الحروف على نطاقين؛ الأول هو كيفية تشكيل الحروف كمجموعة خلاقة ذات وحدة بنيوية، والثاني هو كيفية تمثيل المجموعة هذه بأفضل صورة ممكنة على الشاشة أو على ورق. في جميع الأحوال، ليس هناك أي اعتبار يتأتأ للتطبيقات ثلاثية الأبعاد، ولا حتى في مجال اللافتات.

منذ أن بطلت تقنية سبائك الحروف المعدنية المتحركة، اختفت تقريباً النواحي الثلاثية الأبعاد من الإنتاج الخطي. هذا الأخير هو اليوم سيمفونية معقدة ذات تجلٍ يعتمد نقاطاً أصغر فأصغر. من المذهل أن نرى كم من العبقرية قد وضعها المصممون/ات الخطّيون/ات على مر الوقت في ترتيب النقاط هذه، وذلك بغية خلق أفضل صورة ممكنة عن الخطوط على الشاشة. لقد أصبحت الجهود هذه خارج التداول بفضل الشاشات عالية الدقة المتوافرة اليوم. إلى جانب الظاهرة هذه، بقي نحت السبائك المعدنية ونقشها أقدم التقنيات المتوافرة، غير أنها بقيت حصراً في مجال الحرف اليدوية - بالكاد اهتم المصممون/ات بهذا المضمار. من الصعب تصديق التالي، إلا أن ضمن العدد الهائل من الخطوط الطباعية المتوافرة اليوم، لا يكاد أيّ منها مصمماً بغية الاستعمال الثلاثي الأبعاد بشكل